NVQ/SVQ wo...

FOOD
PREPARATION
& COOKING

To be used in conjunction with the following:

Practical Cookery (seventh edition)
The Theory of Catering (seventh edition)
Questions and Answers on Practical Cookery
Questions and Answers on the Theory of Catering
Candidates Achievement Logbook

*Aims: to develop the knowledge of students
taking NVQ level 2 in Catering and Hospitality
and Food Preparation and Cooking.*

Hodder & Stoughton
LONDON SYDNEY AUCKLAND

Victor Ceserani MBE, CPA, MBA, FHCIMA
Formerly Head of The Ealing School of Hotelkeeping and Catering
and
Professor David Foskett B.Ed(Hons), FHCIMA
Head of Programmes, Thames Valley University, London

British Library Cataloguing in Publication Data

Ceserani, Victor
  NVQ/SVQ Workbook. – Level 2: Food
  Preparation and Cooking
  I. Title II. Foskett, David
  641.5

ISBN 0 340 595094

First published 1993
Impression number 10 9 8 7 6 5 4 3 2 1
Year   1998 1997 1996 1995 1994 1993

Typeset by Wearset, Boldon, Tyne and Wear.
Printed in Great Britain for the educational publishing division of Hodder & Stoughton Ltd, Mill Road, Dunton Green, Sevenoaks, Kent TN13 2YA by Page Bros, Norwich Ltd.

Contents

Introduction

In addition to learning the skills of food preparation and cooking, it is necessary to develop an inquiring mind, a knowledge of catering commodities and the reasons why practical work is carried out in certain ways. The purpose of this workbook is to assist students in developing a systematic approach to combining theory with practical work, which is essential for a proper understanding of catering skills. The book is intended to be used exclusively by the student; it is not intended to be marked by lecturers but students may wish to discuss some of their answers with a knowledgeable person.

Students are advised to develop an attitude of mind so that whenever they are working in practical situations, they are always thinking *why* the various processes are used and *about* the commodities. Similarly, when working through this book, they should be thinking of the practical situation in relation to the theory. The student should never separate theory from practical situations because the two complement each other.

If you wish to test your knowledge further when you complete each element of this workbook, attempt the questions relating to that element which can be found in *Questions and Answers on Practical Cookery* and *Questions and Answers Theory of Catering*. Students will also have a *Candidates Achievement Logbook* which will contain many of the suggested responses to questions asked in this workbook.

Maintain a safe and secure working environment

CARRY OUT PROCEDURES IN THE EVENT OF A FIRE

(Read pp434–9, *The Theory of Catering*)

1 If in doubt about the scale or size of a fire, break the glass on the nearest fire alarm system and telephone the fire brigade.
• What number would you dial for the fire brigade?

....

2 Do not panic but warn other people nearby.
• How would you warn other people?

....

3 Read the fire instructions of your establishment and always follow them.
4 Close all doors and windows and turn off the gas, electricity and ventilating fans.
• What could happen if you fail to close doors and windows?

....

5 Do not wait for the fire to get out of control before calling the fire brigade.
6 Do not risk your own safety or that of others.
7 If the fire is a small one, use the appropriate fire extinguisher.
• What is the correct extinguisher to use on a fat fire?

....

• What is the correct extinguisher to use on a wood, paper, etc, fire?

....

• What is the correct extinguisher to use on fires involving gas?

....

8 Fire fighting equipment must only be used in accordance with laid down procedures.
• Why is a carbon dioxide (CO_2) gas extinguisher not the most efficient way of putting out a fat fire?

....

• What is the colour of the container of a CO_2 extinguisher?

....

9 Safety and emergency signs and notices must be strictly adhered to.
* What is the purpose of a fire blanket?

....

10 Leave the building by the nearest fire escape route and be prepared to assist anyone who may be in need of help. Make for the laid-down assembly point and wait for the roll-call.
* What is the purpose of a roll-call?

....

11 Failure to carry out one or any of the other points may lead to severe damage of property, injury, severe burns and loss of life.
12 Established procedures: it is the responsibility of your employer to see that all relevant procedures in case of fire are made readily available to you; it is your responsibility to ensure that you have read and fully understood what action is required of you in case of fire.

G1.2 CARRY OUT PROCEDURES ON DISCOVERY OF A SUSPICIOUS ITEM OR PACKAGE

1 Any item or package which may give cause for suspicion must be left untouched, e.g. tins, boxes, parcels, carrier bags and holdalls, which may seem strange to you and may be left in a strange place, whether in full-view, part-hidden or hidden.
* If you find a strange sports holdall by/or on top of your locker, should it be treated with suspicion? Why?

....

2 If a suspicious package is found, report it immediately to your departmental head so that prompt action may be taken. The package may contain a bomb or fire explosives. Do not panic! In a calm voice warn others nearby to keep away until the package has been dealt with.
3 Any bag, package or parcel which may be left unattended by a stranger for no apparent reason must be treated as suspicious.
* What would you do if you found a carton of duty-free cigarettes left half-hidden in a corner?

....

4 Resist the temptation to 'take a peep'. It might lead to injury or death to you and those near you.
5 It is your employer's responsibility to make you aware of the correct

health and safety procedures to be followed if a suspicious package is found. It is your responsibility to fully understand and to know what action to take. If you are unsure, consult your trainer or tutor.

G1.3 CARRY OUT PROCEDURES IN THE EVENT OF AN ACCIDENT

Read pp427–34, *The Theory of Catering.*
1 When an accident occurs the member of staff responsible for first aid must be called immediately.
* Name three common types of accidents?

....

....

....

2 If the accident is severe and if a person qualified in first aid is not on the scene, then an ambulance must be called.
* What number should be dialled to call an ambulance? ....
* What is the appropriate action to ensure the safety of injured and non-injured persons?

....

* Why is it important for you to be aware of laid-down procedures in your establishment?

....

3 If you are waiting for a person qualified in first aid to arrive at the scene of the emergency, lie the injured person down and keep him or her warm by covering him or her with a blanket or clothing.
* If an injured person shows signs of faintness, sickness, clammy skin and a pale face, what is the likely conditions or ailment they are suffering? ....
5 All accidents must be reported to the employer and a record of the accident entered in the Accident Book.
* Familiarise yourself with the first-aid procedures in the event of: shock, fainting, cuts, nosebleeds, fractures, burns and scalds, electric shock, gassing (pp432–4, *The Theory of Catering*).

G1.4 MAINTAIN A SAFE ENVIRONMENT FOR CUSTOMERS, STAFF AND VISITORS

1 Read element G1.3 above.

- What is the first thing that should be done in case of an accident to a customer, visitor or member of staff?

....

2   When customers and visitors are in a hotel, they have the right to demand that the premises and procedures used are safe, secure and hygienic. Customers may be staying in the establishment for a holiday or for a visit to a local business centre.
- Name one other reason for staying in your establishment.

....

- Name two other establishments that may receive visitors.

....

3   Fire precautions: customers and visitors should be able to feel confident that all the legally required fire precautions have been complied with and that staff are aware of the correct procedures in case of fire.
- Where should the fire precaution notices be posted in a residential establishment?

....

4   Hygiene: customers and visitors should feel confident and impressed by the standards of care and cleanliness as soon as they enter the outside area of the establishment. Both outside and inside areas and guest rooms should be clean, tidy and in good order. Customers are quick to observe tell-tale signs that the standards of care and hygiene are suspect, e.g. chipped china or glassware, dirty bathrooms or toilets, stained linen, overflowing ash-trays in public areas.
- Name four other examples.

....

5   Remember that you are in a service industry and that your job relies on customers coming to your establishment. They will only return and recommend you if they leave fully satisfied.
6   You should be aware of all health and safety legislation related not only to you, but also to your visitors and customers (pp426–39, *The Theory of Catering*).

G1.5 MAINTAIN A SECURE ENVIRONMENT FOR CUSTOMERS, STAFF AND VISITORS

Keys, property and areas should be secured from unauthorised access at all times. This is not only morally right, but also to comply with the law in order to prevent accidents to customers, staff and visitors.

It is the right of customers, visitors and staff to expect that they and their possessions are safe and secure. Security risks can be caused by:

criminals	terrorists
thieves	muggers
rapists	violent or disturbed people

All property should be properly secured. It is the management's responsibility to carry out the necessary procedures, but equally it is the responsibility of every member of staff to use the security systems correctly at all times.

1   Staff areas and facilities: work areas that have lockable cupboards and drawers should be kept locked and the keys kept in a safe place. Personal valuables are best kept in your locker and the key on your person. However, as lockers can be broken into by a determined thief, it is wise to keep the minimum of cash in your locker and any other personal items of value are best left at home. Petty thieving is a social disease and it is better to be safe than sorry.

•   If you have to bring a large sum of money to work, is it safer to keep it in your locker or on your person?

....

2   Storage areas: because much of the food, drink and equipment stored in hotel and catering establishments is tempting both to the sneak thief and the more practised criminal, all items must be kept under a secure system with a strict control procedure for use as and when required.

Refrigerators and freezers can hold large expensive food items which are an ever-present temptation to the thief, e.g. the cunning thief can quickly take a package, slip it into his or her pocket or wrap it in a tea-cloth and then go to his or her locker in the staff room and hide it away.

•   What particular items of food are vulnerable to theft and why? Give three examples.

....

....

....

3   Cellars and cupboards used for drinks storage are notoriously vulnerable and therefore require vigilance, not only to keep the

stocks intact but also to remove temptation from those who may
have a drink problem.
- Can you name any examples of theft connected with alcoholic
beverages that you have been aware of?

....

....

4   Customer areas: reception, restaurant and bar staff should be
   prepared to ask customers not to leave bags, briefcases or other
   valuable items where they might be taken by an alert thief, e.g.
   unattended on the floor or on a seat. There should be secure
   storage areas for luggage and safe-deposit facilities for money and
   valuables.
   If any guest should leave property behind, e.g. coats, hats,
   umbrellas, it should be handed to the supervisor immediately.
   Guests should feel confident not only that the key and lock to
   their room is secure, but also that the system of collecting and
   handing in of keys when leaving and entering the establishment is
   controlled and secure. If a key is lost, then all items kept under that
   lock and key can be stolen. For security, if a key is stolen or lost,
   then the lock must be changed.
- Why should keys never be left in locks or in odd places such as
   desk drawers?

....

- Name three other places where you have seen keys kept.

....

- Why should keys, property and areas be secured from unauthorised
   access at all times?

....

....

A sound security system practised by all members of staff
communicates itself to the customers as an example of efficiency and
can give a measure of confidence leading to recommendation and
return business.

UNIT G2 *Maintain a professional and hygienic appearance*

MAINTAIN A PROFESSIONAL AND HYGIENIC APPEARANCE

1   To present a smart, clean and tidy image to customers, to prolong the life of the clothes (whether they be supplied or your own) and to ensure safety and hygiene. All clothing worn by staff should be properly looked after.

   In relation to kitchen staff (pp444–5, *The Theory of Catering*):

- Why are chefs' jackets double-breasted and aprons worn below the knees?

....

- Why is it unwise to wear sandals or training shoes in the kitchen?

....

- Why should staff involved in food preparation and cooking wear a head covering?

....

2   All clothing should be clean, in good repair and pressed (where appropriate).

3   Body perspiration and underarm odours can quickly occur, particularly in busy situations and warm rooms. Any suspicion of this is most objectionable to customers, guests and fellow members of staff.

- Excluding the use of body sprays and underarm deodorants, what are the two ways in which this can be avoided?

....

....

4   Trousers, shirts, dresses, jackets and overalls should be kept on proper hangers.

- Why is this necessary?

....

5   Many staff spend a large part of their working time on their feet, so practical, comfortable shoes are essential.

- Calculate the number of hours that you spend on your feet during a working day. ....

Shoes should be: kept clean and in good repair; if lace-up's are worn the laces should always be tied; a second pair of shoes kept at work can help relieve aching feet during a long working day.

6 Correct clothing, footwear and headgear should be worn at all times when on duty in order to:

a. prevent accidents, eg safe shoes in the kitchen protect feet from hot spillage of fat, oil, etc.

b. prevent cross-contamination and infection, eg dirty clothes enable germs to multiply, and if dirty clothing comes into contact with food the food may be contaminated;

c. maintain a clean and professional appearance, eg neat, clean, helpful food service staff will always add to the enjoyment of a meal for a customer;

d. support the company image, eg guests that are impressed with the appearance of the staff inevitably form good opinions about the company and are likely to return – without customers you have no job!;

e. ensure the safety of the person, eg a loose heel on a shoe may come off when you are hurrying downstairs, which may result in you injuring yourself;

f. comply with the law, eg if hair is found in prepared food, the worker is liable to prosecution and a fine.

• Give three examples of incorrect working clothing that you have seen worn.

....

....

....

7 Hair, moustaches and beards are neat and tidy (p441, *The Theory of Catering*).

• Why should food handler's hair be washed regularly and kept covered?

....

• Why should men's hair be kept short?

....

• Why should hair never be scratched or combed by food handlers?

....

8 Jewellery, perfumes and cosmetics should only be worn in

accordance with procedures laid down by your employer.
- What is the risk of a food handler wearing jewellery, eg clip-on earrings?

....

If make-up is used, it should only be used sparingly. If perfumes or aftershave are used by staff working in food preparation areas, they may taint the food.

9 Cuts, grazes, burns, wounds must be correctly treated.
- Should they be kept covered? ....
- If yes, with what should they be covered, and why?

....

10 With certain spots, cuts, and sores there are vast numbers of harmful bacteria which must not be permitted to get on food.
- Should people who have septic spots, cuts, and sores be allowed to handle food, and if not, why not?

....

- What is meant by the word septic?

....

11 Any employee suffering from illness or infection must report this immediately to his or her employer. There are four reasons why illness and infection should be reported; two of them are: to prevent cross-contamination and infection, and to comply with the law.
- What are the other two reasons?

....

....

UNIT 2D10 *Handle and maintain knives*

D10.1   HANDLE AND MAINTAIN KNIVES
Read pp11–17, *Practical Cookery*.
- Give two reasons why knives should be kept sharp.

....

....

- Give two reasons why knives must always be handled correctly.

....

....

- What is the danger associated with using blunt knives?

....

After use, knives should be carefully washed in warm detergent water, thoroughly dried and carefully put away. If possible, knives should be colour coded, the colour denoting the specific usage requirement. Complete the following:

Colour	*Usage*
Brown	Cooked meats
....	Fish (raw)
Red	....
Green	....
White	....

UNIT 2D11 *Accept and store food deliveries*

2D11.1 ACCEPT FOOD DELIVERIES
Read pp281–7, *The Theory of Catering.*
- Why is it important that all food orders be checked on delivery?

....

- Two documents are required to check food deliveries, one is the order that has been given. What is the name of the other document that the delivery person will bring?

....

- There are four reasons why receiving areas should be secured from unauthorised access; two of them are: to prevent accidents and injury, and to prevent vandalism to receiving areas and items. What are the other two?

....

....

- Why is it important that all work is planned and time is appropriately allocated to meet daily schedules?

....

- What should be the procedure if some foods in a delivery are damaged or exceed the sell-by date?

....

- If any of the items delivered have to be returned because of damage, lack of freshness, quality or any other reason, what document should the delivery person sign before taking the items away?

....

1 If deliveries of chilled or frozen foods are made, the temperatures must be checked to ensure that they comply with the temperatures laid down by your employer and then the food must be swiftly transferred to the correct storage cabinets.
2 Once food has been received and signed for it must be handled carefully while it is being transferred to storage cabinets.
3 Delivery documentation must be correctly completed. There are at least two and sometimes three documents used.
- What are these?

....

....

....

- Why is it important to keep all receiving areas clean, tidy and free from rubbish?

....

- How many different storage areas would be required for the correct storage of chilled, frozen, cooked, uncooked, preserved and ambient foods and why?

....

....

- What is the meaning of the word ambient?

....

- How and where should each of the following be stored?
Meat and poultry: ....
Fish: ....
Fruit or vegetables: ....
Eggs: ....
Dairy items: ....
Cakes and biscuits: ....
Dry goods: ....
- State why the following storage conditions are important
Lighting: ....
Ventilation: ....
Temperature: ....
Cleanliness: ....

2D11.2 MAINTAIN FOOD STORES

1 A constant stock of food items should always be maintained to maintain efficiency in the workplace and to maintain sales levels.
- Give two more reasons:

....

....

Read pp281–93, *The Theory of Catering*.
- What documents are used for receiving, storing and issuing food items?

....

....

- Food items should only be issued from the stores on receipt of what?

....

- If any food stocks are low, to whom should it be reported?

....

2 There are five reasons why correct storage and rotation procedures for all foods should be followed: three of them are: to ensure correct temperature of food items is maintained, to ensure food is used in date order or order of quality specifications, and to prevent damage to, and contamination of, products.

- Give two more reasons:

....

....

3 All food storage areas must be regularly cleaned and kept in an orderly fashion.
- Why is this important in relation to health and safety legislation and food hygiene?

....

....

- State how the following items should be stored:
Tea: ....
Sugar: ....
Vacuum-packed vegetables: ....
Canned food: ....
Dairy products: ....
Peeled potatoes: ....

UNIT 2D12 *Clean food production areas, equipment and utensils*

2D12.1 **CLEAN FOOD PRODUCTION AREAS**

Read pp446–78, *The Theory of Catering.*
- Why is it important that work is planned and time appropriately allocated to meet daily schedules?

....

....

1 Sinks and handbasins must be clean and free flowing to satisfy food hygiene regulations.
- What hand washing facilities (separate from food preparation sinks) must also be available in the kitchen?

....

....

2   Work surfaces, tables and cutting boards must be kept clean at all times.
*   How should they be cleaned?

....

....

*   What is the danger if they are not kept clean?

....

....

3   Floors and walls must be clean and the floors kept dry.
*   What is the danger of a wet floor or if fat has been spilled?

....

....

4   Sink waste gullies should be checked and cleaned of any blockages. Traps used to collect tea leaves, grease and other debris need to be emptied and cleaned regularly. Shelves, cupboards and drawers should be emptied and cleaned weekly.
5   Correct cleaning equipment and materials must be used. The cleaning specification should be supplied by your employer, but if ever in doubt about which, or how much, cleaning agent to use, read the manufacturer's instruction on the container.
6   Rubbish should be placed in clean containers and kept covered with a lid. Waste food should be kept in separate clean containers and covered at all times with a lid. Every time containers are emptied, they should be thoroughly washed and dried (p466, *The Theory of Catering*).
*   Why should rubbish not be allowed to accumulate outside a building?

....

....

*   Which is preferable: paper or plastic-lined bins which are destroyed with the rubbish, or un-lined bins? Why?

....

....

*   What is a waste-master?

....

7   There are six good reasons why waste must be handled and disposed of correctly; four of them are: to comply with the law; to

avoid creating a fire hazard; to prevent accidents; and to avoid pollution of the environment.
• Name the other two reasons: ....

....

8   Metal, painted and glass surfaces, floor and wall tiles, and vinyl or linoleum floor coverings must be cleaned to comply with: health and safety legislation; food hygiene legislation and procedures laid down by your establishment.

2D12.2 CLEAN FOOD PRODUCTION EQUIPMENT

Read pp328–61, *The Theory of Catering*.
1   Food production equipment must be correctly turned off and dismantled before and during cleaning.
•   Why is this essential?

....

2   In order to satisfy health, safety and food regulation, equipment must be clean, dry and correctly re-assembled.
•   Why is this essential with gas stoves?

....

3   Always use the correct cleaning equipment and materials as specified by your employer. Equipment must be correctly stored after cleaning.
•   How should saucepans be stored and why?

....

4   Ovens, hobs, ranges, griddles, grids, salamanders, fryers, bains-marie and hotplates must all be cleaned after each service in order to comply with health and safety legislation, food hygiene legislation and all relevant procedures laid down by your employer.

2D12.3 CLEAN FOOD PRODUCTION UTENSILS

Read pp356–64, *The Theory of Catering*.
1   Soiled utensils, ie pots, pans, bowls, dishes, moulds, whisks, sieves, colanders, strainers, spoons, ladles, slicers, graters, peelers, zesters, corers and tin openers should be washed in hot detergent water, rinsed in clean water, thoroughly dried and correctly stored.

- Why should strainers and sieves be washed immediately after each use?

....

- If saucepans are difficult to clean, what is the best procedure to use before washing them?

....

- Why should scouring pads never be used on stainless steel?

....

- Why should wooden items never be allowed to soak in water?

....

2   Draw a refuse compacter and label the working parts (if necessary, ask your tutor for help).

UNIT 2D1 *Prepare and cook meat and poultry dishes*

2D1.1 **PREPARE MEAT FOR COOKING**

Read pp51–7, *The Theory of Catering.*
- Why is it important that food preparation areas and equipment are clean and satisfy health, safety and hygiene regulations? ....

....

- Explain fully the following:

Contamination:

....

....

Pest infestation:

....

....

Cleanliness:

....

....

1   Preparation methods
- What is the purpose of trimming meat when preparing it for cooking?

....

- What should be done with the trimmings?

....

- Accepting that knives are clean, what else should be done to them before trimming and dicing meat?

....

- Name four dishes for which beef would be diced.

....

....

- When dicing meat, there are three important points to be borne in mind.
  Remove ....

Cut ....

Remove excess ....

- Which of the following meat joints are tied with string in order to retain their shape while cooking? Tick your answer.
  Best-end or rack of lamb.
  7 lb joint of braised beef.
  Boned stuffed shoulder of lamb.
  10 lb rib of beef.

- What is the reason for rolling certain meat joints?

....

- Name two joints that can be prepared by rolling.

....

- Stuffing of certain meat joints is a means of adding extra flavour, seasoning and variety. Name three meat joints suitable for stuffing.

....

....

- List the ingredients of a suitable stuffing for each of the three meat joints:

....

....

- After stuffing a meat joint, what else must be done before it is ready for cooking and why?

....

- Certain cuts of meat are batted either to: get them to a required shape; get them to a required thickness or thinness; or to tenderise them. What veal cut would be batted out thinly?

....

- For what beef or veal dish would lean slices of beef or veal be batted out thinly?

....

- Barding is the covering of certain lean, tender pieces or joints of meat with thin slices of fat bacon before cooking. What is the purpose of a bard? ....

- Why is it essential to tie a bard in place before cooking?

....

- Name two joints or cuts of meat that might be barded.

....

- What is the correct method of preparing wing rib of beef for roasting? (Give your answer, then check it with p276, *Practical Cookery*.)

....

....

- Always check recipes to see what other ingredients are required to be prepared either to be cooked separately or combined with the meat. What other ingredients may be used in addition to meat for: Steak and kidney pie:

....

....

Boiled silverside of beef:

....

....

Beef stroganoff:

....

....

Mixed grill:

....

....

....

Shish kebab:

....

....

....

Lamb hot-pot:

....

....

2 Food hygiene (pp453–78, *The Theory of Catering*).
- There are eight main contamination threats when preparing and storing uncooked meat. Four are concerned with the transfer of food poisoning bacteria. Describe these in detail.

....

....

....

....

- The remaining four are concerned with: uncovered food; disposal and storage; storage temperatures; and thawing procedures. Describe each of these in detail.

....

....

....

- Give two reasons why preparation work must be planned and sufficient time allocated to meet daily schedules.

....

....

- If the meat ordered is not of the correct type, quality and quantity required, what could be the result in each case?
  Incorrect type, eg beef chuck steak for beef olives:

....

....

Cheapest quality:

....

....

Incorrect quantity:

....

....

- Ensure that not only the correct equipment is used, but also the correct size of equipment. Why is this important (give two examples and reasons)?

....

....

- What are the risks if preparation areas and equipment are not correctly cleaned?

....

....

....

....

3 Preparation of beef (pp270–7, *Practical Cookery*).

• Name the eight joints in a hindquarter of beef and give a use for each joint:

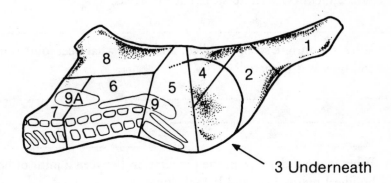

3 Underneath

Diagram of hindquarter of beef showing meat joints.

1 ....
2 ....
3 ....
4 ....
5 ....
6 ....
7 ....
8 ....

• What two joints are not shown on the above diagram?

....

• How is beef assessed for quality?

....

• Name three beef joints suitable for roasting.

....

• What are the three essential points of preparation required for a joint of beef to be roasted?

....

....

....

- What is the traditional joint of beef used for boiling and how is it prepared?

....

....

- What thickness is rump steak cut for steaks?

....

- Why is a minute steak so called, and from what beef joint is it cut and how is it prepared?

....

....

- What is the difference in the preparation between a joint of beef for boiling English style and French style?

....

....

- How is beef cut for beef stroganoff?

....

- How is beef cut for beef carbonnade?

....

4   Preparation of veal (pp301–5, *Practical Cookery*).
- From which joint of veal are the best escalopes cut?

....

- Describe the preparation of a veal escalope for Viennoise?

....

- How is the meat prepared for a veal sauté?

....

- How is a breast of veal prepared for roasting?

....

- What is the difference in preparation of the meat for a fricassée and a blanquette of veal?

....

....

- What is the difference in meat preparation between escalopes for Viennoise and Madère?

....

- How is the meat prepared to make a veal pojarski?

....

5 Preparation of lamb and mutton (pp241–6, *Practical Cookery*).
- When preparing lamb and mutton joints, why are some or all bones sometimes removed?

....

....

- Name the seven joints and give a use for each joint.

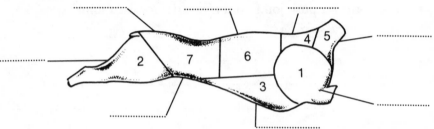

Diagram of lamb carcass showing meat joints.

- How is a quality lamb carcass assessed?

....

- How many bones are there in a shoulder of lamb?

....

- What is the difference between lamb and mutton?

....

- Describe the preparation of a loin of lamb for stuffing and roasting.

....

- What is the difference between a loin chop and a Barnsley chop? What could be another name for a Barnsley chop?

....

- Describe the preparation of a best-end (rack) of lamb for roasting.

....

- Name three boneless cuts of lamb.

....

- How is meat prepared for a hot-pot?

....

6 Preparation of pork (pp322–4, *Practical Cookery*).

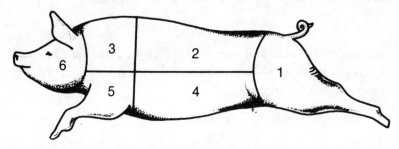

Diagram of pig carcass showing meat joints.

- Name the six pork joints and give a use for each joint.

....

....

....

....

....

....

- What are the four quality points for pork?

....

....

- What is meant by 'scoring a joint of pork'?

....

- What herb is traditionally used for seasoning a boned belly of pork before rolling?

....

- How is meat prepared for sweet and sour pork?

....

7 Preparation of bacon (pp331–2, *Practical Cookery*).

- Name the five bacon joints and give an example of use for each joint.

....

....

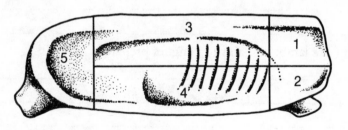

Diagram of side of bacon showing meat joints.

- What are the five signs of quality in a side of bacon?

- What are the two ways of preparing a hock of bacon for boiling?

- Why is it usually necessary to soak bacon joints before boiling?

- Which bacon does not require soaking?

- What is the name of the bone in a gammon which if it is not removed will hinder carving?

8 Preparation of offal (pp247, 277, 305, 324, *Practical Cookery*).
- What basic preparation is required for beef, lamb, veal and pigs kidneys?

- How are kidneys prepared for sauté?

- How is lamb, veal and pigs liver prepared for cooking?

- What is the preparation for lamb and veal sweetbreads?

....

....

....

- How are lamb, veal and ox tongues prepared?

....

....

....

- How is tripe prepared for cooking?

....

....

....

9 Recipes.
- Describe either a lamb or beef dish of your choice, list the ingredients and explain why you choose this particular recipe (it may be that it features on the menu where you work, or one for which you have made up the recipe).

....

....

....

....

....

....

....

....

....

....

....

....

....

....

....

....

....

....

....

....

....

....

....

....

....

- If you work in the industry, list any variations or differences you have experienced compared to what is listed in the text in this element or from what you have learnt from your tutor.

....

....

....

....

....

....

....

....

....

....

....

....

....

....

....
....
....
....
....
....
....
....
....
....
....
....
....
....
....
....
....
....

2D1.2 PREPARE POULTRY FOR COOKING

1   The term poultry is applied to all domestic fowl used for food:
    chicken, turkeys, ducks, geese and pigeons (pp73, 76–80, *The
    Theory of Catering*).
*   What is the difference between a battery-reared and free-range
    chicken?

....

2   Preparation methods.
a. Washing: before preparing poultry for cooking whole, the insides
    must be checked for cleanliness and washed thoroughly under cold
    running water if necessary.
*   Why is this so important?

....

b. Skinning: for certain dishes, eg supremes, kebabs, the skin is removed by pulling it off firmly with the fingers and carefully cutting any holding sinews if necessary.

- For what purposes are chicken skinned in your establishment?

....

c. Trimming: it is usual to trim chicken pieces in order to neaten the shape. In older fowls it may be necessary to remove fat.
- What are chicken trimmings of skin and bone used for?

....

- What should be done with chicken fat?

....

d. Jointing (pp345–8, *Practical Cookery*).
- In to how many pieces is a $2\frac{1}{2}$ lb chicken usually cut for sauté?

....

- What is the difference between a suprême and a ballotine of chicken?
- Draw a supreme and a ballotine.

e. Trussing or tieing (pp344–6, *Practical Cookery*).
- Before trussing a chicken or turkey for roasting, why is it sensible to remove the wishbone?

....

- When not in use, how can the sharp point of the trussing needle be protected?

....

f. Batting: when preparing suprêmes of chicken and escalopes of chicken or turkey, a meat bat and a little water may be used to help give shape or/and thinness.
g. Barding: a bard is a thin slice of fat bacon which is used to cover the tender parts (breasts) of birds before roasting. The bard should be tied on with string.
h. Dicing: for certain dishes of chicken and turkey, eg stir-fry, kebabs, the birds are skinned and all the bones are removed and the meat neatly diced. The white and dark meat should be kept separately.
- Why should the white and dark meat be kept separate?

....

i.   Marinating: a marinade is a mixture of spices, herbs, vegetables and
     a liquid, eg red wine, soy sauce, and is used to give flavour and
     sometimes helps to tenderise the meat.
*   Give two examples of marinades used for chicken.

....

3   Food hygiene (pp453–77, *The Theory of Catering*).
*   What is cross-contamination and why is it so essential to take all
     possible steps to avoid it when preparing poultry?

....

....

....

*   What is salmonella?

....

*   Salmonella is present in approximately 20, 40, or 60 per cent of
     raw and frozen chicken?

....

*   Why should fresh uncooked chicken and cooked roast chicken not
     be stored together?

....

*   What is the danger of using the same preparation areas, equipment
     and utensils for preparing cooked and uncooked poultry?

....

*   What is another name for bacteria? ....
*   What is the danger to health if unhygienic equipment, utensils and
     preparation methods are used when handling poultry.

....

*   What examples of unhygienic equipment and preparation methods
     have you seen, and what would be your remedy (pp450–1, *The
     Theory of Catering*)?

....

4   Pests (pp465–8, *The Theory of Catering*).
*   How can rats, mice, flies, cockroaches and other vermin
     contaminate uncovered food?

....

5   Storage.
*   What is the correct way to store waste and unused food items from

the kitchen and, what are the dangers if this is not done correctly?

....

....

6 Thawing (pp76, 284, *The Theory of Catering*).
* What are the main contamination dangers of storing poultry at incorrect temperatures and incorrect thawing procedures when using frozen poultry?

....

....

* What is the correct way to defrost frozen chicken?

....

....

* If chicken suprêmes are required to be prepared for lunch and frozen chicken are delivered at 10 am, what is likely to happen?

....

....

....

* What examples (if any) of inefficiency have you observed in the use and preparation of poultry?

....

....

....

7 Preparation of chicken (pp344–8, *Practical Cookery*).
* List four signs of quality in chicken.

....

....

* What is meant by eviscerating?

....

* What is a suitable weight of chicken for cutting for sauté?

....

* Briefly describe the preparation of a chicken for grilling?

....

* What is a suitable weight of chicken for suprêmes?

....

- Why are the fillets lifted from suprêmes and what then happens to them? ....
- How is a chicken ballotine prepared?

....

- Draw a chicken prepared for spatchcock. Show the difference in a chicken cut for crapaudine.

- State how each would appear in a menu.

....

....

- Describe a chicken dish of your choice, list the ingredients and explain why you have chosen this particular recipe.

....

....

....

2D1.3 COOK MEAT AND POULTRY DISHES

1   At all times before, during and after cooking, the following points must be borne in mind:

a.   Cooking areas and equipment are ready for use and satisfy health, safety and hygiene regulations.

b.   Work is planned and sufficient time is allocated to meet daily schedules.

c.   Meat or poultry is cooked according to customer and recipe requirements.

d.   Meat and poultry dishes are finished and presented according to customer and dish requirements.

e.   Preparation and cooking areas and equipment are correctly cleaned after use.

f.   If any unexpected situation should occur, appropriate action must be taken within the individual's responsibility.

g.   All work should be carried out in an organised and efficient manner taking account of priorities and laid-down procedures.

2 Roasting (pp57–60, *Practical Cookery*).
- Describe the two methods of roasting and their variations.

....

....

- List five advantages of roasting

....

....

....

....

....

- Name the important points in making a roast gravy.

....

- How is roast gravy made in your establishment and, if it is different from the traditional method, why is this so?

....

....

....

- Which are the only two meats which are sometimes cooked and served pink?

....

....

- When cooking roast beef, what fat should be used to make Yorkshire puddings and why?

....

....

- When roasting pork, how can the crackling be made crisp?

....

- When roasting veal, how can the flavour be increased during the cooking?

....

- What is the traditional difference between roast gravy for beef and veal?

....

- Why should roast chickens be cooked on their sides rather than with the breasts uppermost?

....

- How is a roast chicken tested to see if it is cooked?

....

- Why is frequent basting recommended when roasting meat or poultry?

....

- What are the five important points to be observed when roasting?

....

....

....

....

....

- Complete the following table:

	Approximate cooking times	Degree of cooking
Beef	.... min per ½ kg (1 lb) and ...... min over	Underdone
Lamb	.... min per ½ kg (1 lb) and ...... min over	Cooked through
Lamb	.... min per ½ kg (1 lb) and ...... min over	Cooked pink
Mutton	.... min per ½ kg (1 lb) and ...... min over	Cooked through
Veal	.... min per ½ kg (1 lb) and ...... min over	Cooked through
Pork	.... min per ½ kg (1 lb) and ...... min over	Thoroughly cooked

Insert the required cooking times for each of these meats.

- Approximate roasting times for chicken or turkey are 15–20 minutes per lb. True or false?

....

- What is a meat thermometer and what is its purpose (pp53, 394, *The Theory of Catering*)?

....

- Why are roast joints set on a trivet in the roasting tray?

....

- Name two types of trivet.

....

....

- Without the use of a meat thermometer, how can meat be tested to ensure it is cooked through?

....

- Why is it important to time the cooking of roasts in order to let them rest after they are cooked and before carving?

....

....

- Why is it important to carefully conserve the meat sediment in a roasting tray after the joint is used?

....

3 Grilling (pp60–3, *Practical Cookery*).
- Name three methods of grilling and give the variations in each case.

....

....

....

- Why must grills be pre-heated and lightly oiled prior to use?

....

- Complete the first column in the following table:

Degrees of cooking grills		Appearance of juice issuing from the meat when pressed
....	*au bleu*	Red and bloody
....	*saignant*	Reddish pink
....	*à point*	Pink
....	*bien cuit*	Clear

Insert the missing words to describe the degree of cooking.

- Name four items which when grilling under the salamander it is sensible to put on trays and why.

....

....

....

- Give four general rules for efficient grilling.

....

....

....

- List four safety rules when grilling.

....

....

....

- Name four combinations of food suitable for cooking as brochettes.
  Lamb ....
  Peppers ....
  Monk fish ....

  ....

- Name two suggestions for marinades for brochettes.

....

....

- On a bed of what are brochettes usually served?

....

- What is the final finish for devilled grilled chicken?

....

4 Barbecuing is grilling on pre-heated, greased bars over a fierce heat, e.g. gas, charcoal or wood. When using a solid fuel, the flames and smoke must be allowed to die down before placing food on the bars, otherwise the food will be tainted and spoiled. Certain foods, eg brochettes or chicken, may be marinaded before cooking. Other foods, eg pork spare ribs, are brushed liberally with a barbecue sauce on both sides during cooking (p326, *Practical Cookery*).

5 Tandoori cooking is named after the unusual clay oven called the *tandoor* (p46, *The Theory of Catering*), which produces slightly charred spiced chicken and lamb dishes. Tandoor meats are first marinaded to flavour and tenderise them; many of the marinades

contain a red colouring agent. Foods to be cooked are placed on long spits and positioned vertically inside the oven. The meats are first seared with high heat, then the marinade is applied repeatedly and allowed to dry on the surface, leaving a residue that forms a crust and seals the juices in the meat.

If a traditional tandoor is not available then an oven grill, rôtisserie or barbecue can be used provided the basic rules and principles of tandoori cooking are applied.

Example of a tandoori chicken recipe
$1\frac{1}{4}$–$1\frac{1}{2}$ kg ($2\frac{1}{2}$–3 lb) chicken cut as for sauté
1 teaspoon salt
Juice of 1 lemon
12 fluid ozs plain yoghurt
1 small chopped onion
1 peeled clove garlic
5 cm (2 in) piece ginger peeled and
    quartered
$\frac{1}{2}$ fresh hot green chilli, sliced
2 teaspoons garam masala
1 teaspoon ground cumin
Few drops each red and yellow colouring

Combine in blender or processor

1   Cut slits bone deep in the chicken pieces.
2   Sprinkle the salt and lemon juice on both sides of the pieces, lightly rubbing into the slits; leave for 20 minutes.
3   Brush the chicken pieces on both sides ensuring the marinade goes into the slits. Cover and refrigerate for 6–24 hours.
4   Pre-heat oven to maximum temperature.
5   Shake off as much of the marinade as possible from the chicken pieces, place on skewers and bake for 15–20 minutes or until cooked. Serve with red onion rings and lime or lemon wedges.

6   Shallow frying (pp64–7, *Practical Cookery*).

• When shallow frying foods, why should the presentation side be fried first?

• What is the difference between a frying and a sauté pan?

• Why is correctly deglazing a pan after frying meat or poultry so important?

- Describe the deglazing process in detail.

....

- Describe the difference between a sauté of beef and a ragoût of beef.

....

- What pre-preparation is required for a griddle before using it for cooking?

....

- Name four foods that may be cooked on a griddle.

....

....

- What is stir-frying? ....

....

- What is the traditional pan used for stir frying? ....
- What substitute for the traditional stir fry pan can be used?

....

- How is meat or chicken usually cut for stir frying? ....

....

- Draw a wok pan.

- How does a wok stove differ from a traditional stove?

....

- Ask your tutor or trainer why the Chinese developed stir fry.
- Name a popular cut of lamb that is shallow fried and the type of pan traditionally used.

....

- When cooking a sauté of kidneys, why are the kidneys drained in a colander after they are cooked and the drained off liquid discarded?

....

- Why should kidneys not be re-boiled after being sautéed, drained and placed in a sauce?

....

- Name two liquids which may be used to deglaze a pan in which kidneys have been fried.

- What is the usual accompaniment to a beef stroganoff?

- What does the word bordelaise mean in relation to a sirloin steak?

- Suggest three interesting ways of cooking and serving a tournedo.

- When cooking a chicken sauté, why are the leg pieces cooked for a little longer than the breast pieces?

- What is the difference between chicken sauté chasseur and chicken sauté with mushrooms?

- What does the word Parmentier indicate when used as chicken sauté Parmentier?

7 Braising (pp47–50, *Practical Cookery*).
- What is the essential difference between braising and roasting meat?

- What are the two basic methods of braising (give an example of meat or poultry cooked by each).

- What is the first cooking procedure when braising meat, and why is the procedure necessary?

- Describe why braising is a suitable method of cookery for less tender joints of meat.

- Give two advantages of braising meats and poultry.

- Should cooking liquid for braising boil rapidly, boil steadily, simmer gently or barely simmer?

Give the reasons why for your answer.

....

....

• What type of pans or oven-proof dishes should be used for braising?

....

• Once a joint has come to the boil, what is an ideal oven temperature for cooking?

....

• Name a piece of large equipment suitable for braising for use in large-scale catering.

....

• Describe how braised joints of meat can be glazed.

....

• What other ingredients are added to a joint of beef to be braised?

....

• When braising a joint, how far up should liquid be added?

....

• Name two joints of beef suitable for braising.

....

• Why have you chosen these two joints?

....

....

• How are vegetables prepared before they are added to a braised joint?

....

• When serving, should braised beef be cut in thick or thin slices?

....

• Name two suitable garnishes for braised beef.

....

• How thick should steaks for braising be cut?

....

• Name a traditional sauce served with braised ox tongue.

....

- What is a popular vegetable cooked in and served with ox liver?

....

- What is the usual pre-preparation for braised shoulder of veal?

....

- When braising a duck with peas, what two other ingredients are usually added as part of the garnish?

....

8 Stewing (pp44–7, *Practical Cookery*).
- Give the definition for stewing.

....

- Why is stewing suitable for cheaper cuts of meat and poultry?

....

- Name three ways in which stews can be thickened?

....

- What are the two ways in which stews may be cooked?

....

....

- What is the effect of the stewing process on meat?

....

....

- Give five advantages of stewing meat.

....

....

....

....

- What is the ideal cooking temperature for stewing and how could you describe it without giving figures?

....

- Give four signs that a stew has overcooked.

....

....

....

....

- If a hot pan is taken out of the oven, how can it be marked as a warning to others that it is hot?

....

- What is the traditional Hungarian dish of stewed beef with paprika called?

....

- What is the traditional garnish for this dish?

....

- What other ingredients are added to the dish of stewed mutton and haricot beans called haricot mutton?

....

- There are many variations of an Irish stew. List a typical set of ingredients.

....

- Why is the meat for Irish stew and any other white stew blanched and refreshed before use?

....

- Name two optional accompaniments to Irish stew.

....

- What is the name given to a dish of chicken pieces cooked in a white sauce?

....

- What would be a typical garnish to this dish?

....

- How should a liaison be used in this dish and what is its purpose?

....

- What is tripe?

....

- What is an approximate cooking time for tripe and onions?

....

- Name three different ways of thickening a dish of tripe.

....

....

....

9   Boiling (pp38–41, *Practical Cookery*).
- Name four liquids in which foods can be boiled.

....

....

- Why, when boiling meats, is it important to boil gently?

....

- What is another name for boiling gently?

....

- What would be the difference in the texture of meat if a joint is allowed to boil quickly rather than gently?

....

- Give five advantages of boiling meat.

....

....

....

....

....

- What are the advantages of starting to boil food in cold liquid, brought to the boil and allowed to boil gently?

....

- What are the advantages of adding food to boiling liquid, re-boiling and allowing to boil gently?

....

- Why is it important to skim the surface of the liquid frequently during the boiling of meat or poultry?

....

- In addition to carrots and onions, what is the traditional ingredient cooked in and served with silverside of beef?

....

- What is the difference between beef boiled English and French style?

....

- Should silverside of beef be carved with or against the grain?

....

- What is the approximate cooking time per pound for boiled beef?

....

- Name six vegetables that are traditionally cooked in with French-style boiled beef?

....

....

....

- Name the traditional sauce served with boiled leg of lamb or mutton.

....

- From what basic stock is this sauce made?

....

- What other ingredients are added when boiling a chicken?

....

- Name the traditional sauce served with boiled chicken.

....

- Name and describe the method of producing the traditional accompaniment to boiled chicken.

....

- How is a boiled chicken tested to ensure that it is cooked?

....

10 Hygiene (see pp453–68 *Theory of Catering*).
11 Dishes. List two dishes in each category you have recently prepared.
    Roast ....
    Braised ....
    Stews ....

- Describe the presentation of one in each category.

....

....

....

....

....

....

UNIT 2D2 *Prepare and cook fish dishes*

PREPARE FISH FOR COOKING

Read pp86–109, *The Theory of Catering*.

1   Before considering fish preparation, the following points need to be understood and carried out:

a.   Preparation areas and equipment are ready for use and satisfy health, safety and hygiene regulations.

b.   Work is planned and appropriate time is allocated to meet schedules.

c.   Fish is of the correct type, quality and quantity.

d.   Fish is correctly prepared according to dish requirements.

e.   Where appropriate, prepared fish is combined with other ingredients ready for cooking.

f.   Appropriate equipment for cooking is ready for use.

g.   Preparation areas and equipment are correctly cleaned after use.

h.   All work is carried out in an organised and efficient manner.

•   Name four round and four flat fish.

....

....

2   Fish may be delivered either:

a.   whole, uncleaned and certain fish, eg salmon, with the scales on;

b.   whole, cleaned (gutted) but with the head and scales on;

c.   filleted, with or without skins.

•   Irrespective of the type of fish and the way it is to be prepared why is careful washing and draining essential?

....

3   With most fish, trimming of some kind is required. If the fish is to be served whole, then the scales must be removed, the fins are cut off using fish scissors and, if the head is to be left on, the gills and eyes are removed (in traditional French cookery, the eyes are not removed).

4   Fish fillets need to be checked for any bones that may remain and any discoloured parts cut away.

5   Basic fish preparation (pp206–7, 208–9, 217 (recipe 23), 221 (recipes 32, 36), 222 (recipe 37), 224 (recipe 47), *Practical Cookery*).

•   Is it necessary to remove the head of plaice before filleting? ....

- When filleting flat fish, do you work from head to tail or from tail to head?

....

- Do you start on the back or belly side when filleting round fish?

....

6   Portioning (pp210–11, *Practical Cookery*)
- What is an approximate weight of fish per portion, on the bone and off the bone?

....

- What would be the number of pieces of the following cuts that would be served as a portion?

Darne of salmon ....   Supreme of salmon ....
Tronçon of turbot ....   Paupiette of sole ....
Fillet of plaice ....   Goujons of plaice ....

- Why should all portions of fish be the same weight or as near to that weight as possible?

....

7   Baking (p210, *Practical Cookery*).
- Name three fish or cuts of fish that are suitable for stuffing.

....

- Suggest a suitable stuffing for each.

....

....

8   Hygiene (see also pp453–68 *Theory of Catering*).
- What are the main contamination threats when storing raw fish?

....

....

....

- What is the main threat from storing fish at incorrect temperatures.

....

- What is the threat from thawing frozen fish incorrectly?

....

- What is the contamination threat from unclean fish?

....

2D2.2 COOK FISH DISHES

1 Before any cooking starts, the following points need to be observed (Enlarge on the importance of each):

a. Preparation and cooking areas and equipment are ready and satisfy health, safety and hygiene regulations.

....

b. Work is planned and time is allocated to meet daily schedules.

....

c. Fish dishes are correctly cooked and presented according to customer requirements.

....

d. Preparation and cooking areas and equipment are correctly cleaned after use.

....

e. All work is carried out in an organised and efficient manner.

....

2 Baking (p210, *Practical Cookery*).
* Describe a method of baking a whole fish, eg a sea bass 500 g (1 lb) weight.

....

* Describe how you would stuff and bake 48 portions of cod.

....

....

* Describe how you would stuff and bake fillets of plaice.

....

3 Grilling (pp216–19, *Practical Cookery*).
* Describe the preparation of fish for grilling.

....

* What is the test to ensure that grilled darnes of cod or salmon are cooked? ....
* Before grilling a whole fish, e.g. herring, what preparation is carried out to ensure that it cooks through?

....

* What are the three different ways of grilling fish?

....

- What is the traditional sauce served with grilled herring?

....

- How does the preparation of mackerel for grilling differ from herring?

....

- After grilling whole plaice, which side is presented to the customer?

....

- Why before grilling Dover soles and plaice do you only remove the black skin from the soles?

....

- Suggest two suitable accompaniments to grilled fish.

....

- What are the traditional accompaniments to grilled salmon?

....

4   Frying (pp215–6 and 219–23, *Practical Cookery*).
- What is the difference between shallow fried fish and fish shallow fried meunière?

....

- Before slicing lemon for garnish meunière, why is it important to remove the peel and pith and then the pips?

....

- Why is it important to cook the presentation side of shallow fried fish?

....

- Would it be incorrect to shallow fry and serve fish without the meunière finish?

....

- Name three different fats or oils suitable for shallow fried fish.

....

....

....

- How can you tell when butter is cooked to the nut brown (beurre noisette) stage?

....

- Describe five classical variations to fish meunière or variations that you have developed or used in your own place of work.
1 Garnish belle meunière is ....
2 .... is turned cucumbers
3 .... is flaked almonds
4 Grenobloise is ....
5 ....

Your variations: ....

....

....

....

....

- If required to cook turbot or brill meunière, how would you cut the fish?

....

- Given the choice of serving four portions of fillets of plaice meunière on a silver flat or plates, which would you choose and why?

....

- Suggest three suitable accompaniments for deep fried fish?

....

- Give the ingredients for three different types of frying batter.

....

....

....

5 Fried fish (pp134–6, *The Theory of Catering*, and pp219–23, *Practical Cookery*).
- What is an essential requirement for a fat or oil to be suitable for deep-frying?

....

- What will happen to the food being fried if the frying medium smokes at a low temperature?

....

- Why must any frying medium be free from moisture?

....

- With regard to frying, what do you understand by 'flash point'?

....

- Name four points that indicate when a frying medium should be discarded.

....

....

- Why is fish coated before being deep-fried?

....

- Name three different ways of coating fish before deep-frying.

....

....

....

- Before deep-frying fillets of plaice, both white and black skins should be removed. True or false? ....
- Would there be any difference in the frying temperature for cooking fried sole, goujons of plaice and whitebait and, if so, why?

....

- What is rockfish?

....

- What is the pre-preparation for fish to be cooked à l'Orly and what sauce accompanies the dish?

....

- What are whitebait?

....

- Describe the preparation, cooking and serving of whitebait.

....

6 Poaching (pp42–4, *Practical Cookery*).
- Why is it important when poaching fish, to keep the amount of liquid to the minimum?

....

- Name four liquids in which fish can be poached?

....

....

- What fish is usually poached in milk?

....

- Describe the procedure for making a sauce from the cooking liquid after fish have been poached. ....
....

- When poaching fish, why is time and temperature control so important?
....

- Turbot may be poached whole, cut in slices on the bone or in portions off the bone. Give the correct name and a way in which it could appear on a menu for:
1   a slice of turbot on the bone: ....
2   a portion of turbot off the bone: ....
- Describe the method of poaching and serving slices of turbot on the bone. ....
....

- Does the method of poaching slices of halibut cod or brill on the bone differ from turbot and, if so, how?
....

- What is the term used for a slice of salmon on the bone, and what is the most suitable sized fish from which to cut slices?
....

- What is a court-bouillon, give a suitable recipe and name the fish it is usually connected with?
....
....

- Describe the preparation and cooking of a whole uncleaned salmon.
....
....
....

- When a whole salmon is cooked should it be removed from the cooking liquid at once or allowed to cool in the liquid? (Give reasons for your answer.)
....

- Should a whole salmon cook rapidly or gently and what would be an approximate cooking time for a 14 lb fish?
....

- Suggest two suitable sauces to accompany hot poached salmon.

....

- Describe the preparation, cooking and serving of cod duglére or a similar dish you are familiar with.

....

....

....

- Name six other fish suitable for cooking duglére.

....

....

- What is the difference between a dish of fish with white wine sauce and fish Véronique?

....

- Describe the preparation, cooking and service of fillets of fish Mornay.

....

....

- What is the difference between fish Mornay and fish Florentine?

....

- What are the ingredients for a fish kedgeree?

....

- In addition to haddock, what fish is used for kedgeree?

....

- When a poached smoked haddock is cooked what should be removed before serving?

....

- Describe the cooking and finish of skate with black butter.

....

....

- Describe the preparation and cooking of fish cakes.

....

....

- Give a recipe for fish pie.

....

....

....

....

(Now read pp223–32, *Practical Cookery*.)
7 Steaming (pp50–3, *Practical Cookery*, and pp336–7, 404–5, *The Theory of Catering*.)
- All fish which is poached or boiled may be steamed. True or false?

....

- Describe low pressure, high pressure and sous-vide methods of steaming.

....

....

....

....

- What are the advantages of sous-vide cookery?

....

....

....

- What is the name given to the detailed preparation, cooking and serving of a suitable fish dish cooked sous-vide.

- List six advantages of steaming.

....

....

....

....

....

- What is an essential safety precaution to observe before opening a steamer door after use?

....

- Read pp86–109, *The Theory of Catering*, and answer the questions on pp27–31, *Questions and Answers on The Theory of Catering*.
- Read pp204–38, *Practical Cookery*, and answer the questions on pp69–73, *Questions and Answers on Practical Cookery*.
- With the aid of a drawing, show the presentation of a fish dish you have recently served at your college or place of work. (You may like to show how you could vary the presentation – your tutor or trainer will advise you if necessary.)

UNIT 2D3   *Prepare and cook egg custard based desserts*

2D3.1 **PREPARE AND COOK EGG CUSTARD BASED DESSERTS**
Read pp124–8, *The Theory of Catering*.

- Give three points of quality and freshness for eggs.

....

....

....

- Draw and explain in words what happens to the white and yolk of an egg if it is kept for too long.

- Why should eggs not be stored near strong smelling foods, such as cheese, onions and fish?

....

- In how many sizes are hens' eggs available?

....

- What is salmonella infection and how can it be passed into hens' eggs?

....

- With regard to the dangers of salmonella infection, what is the advantage of using pasteurised egg and in how many forms is pasteurised egg available?

....

....

- Most salmonella infections cause only a mild stomach upset, but the effects can be serious on two types of the population. Name these.

....

- Does the pasteurisation of eggs affect their keeping or ingredient quality?

....

- List the seven points in the Code of Practice recommended by the DHSS and the egg producers for handling eggs.

....

....

....

....

....

....

....

1 Before commencing and during working with eggs the following points must be observed.
a. Preparation areas and equipment are ready for use and satisfy health, safety and hygiene regulations.
b. Work is planned and appropriate time allocated to meet daily schedules.
c. Dessert ingredients are of the type, quality and quantity required.
d. Ingredients are prepared and cooked according to recipe requirements.
e. Desserts are correctly finished and presented according to customer and dish requirements.
f. Finished desserts not for immediate consumption are correctly stored.
g. Preparation and cooking areas and equipment are correctly cleaned after use.
2 Trifle is perhaps one of the most traditional and popular English

desserts for which there are numerous variations. A trifle consists of
lightly soaked sponge cake coated with a lightly thickened egg
custard and liberally decorated with whipped cream and, e.g.
almonds and glacé cherries. A little sherry is sometimes used in
soaking the sponge and fruit, e.g. strawberries, raspberries
incorporated and used in the decoration.

The recipe in *Practical Cookery* makes use of custard powder in
place of eggs, but the following recipe is taken from the author's
Contemporary Cookery.

500 ml	1 pt	milk
		1 vanilla pod or 2–3 drops natural vanilla essence
		2 eggs plus 2 egg yolks *or* 8 egg yolks
50 g	2 oz	castor sugar
200 g	8 oz	sponge cake
150 g	6 oz	raspberry or strawberry jam
60 ml	⅛ pt	medium or sweet sherry
250 ml	½ pt	double cream, whipped
50 g	2 oz	flaked, sliced or nibbed almonds (toasted)
		4 or 8 glacé cherries

1 Heat milk with vanilla pod, cover with a lid, then remove from heat
   and stand for 15 mins. Remove vanilla pod.
2 Thoroughly whisk eggs and sugar in a basin.
3 Boil the milk, add a quarter to the eggs whisking continuously.
4 Add remainder of the milk and clean the saucepan.
5 Return eggs and milk to the clean pan and cook over a gentle heat,
   stirring continuously with a wooden spoon, until the mixture thickens.
6 Immediately remove from the heat. Strain the mixture into a clean
   basin and allow to cool, stirring occasionally.
7 Spread sponge cake with jam, cut into small squares and place in a
   4-portion trifle bowl or individual dishes.
8 Sprinkle on the sherry, allow to soak in.
9 Pour the custard over the sponge cake and allow to set.
10 Decorate with whipped cream, almonds and halves of cherries.

Notes 100 g (4 oz) lightly crushed macaroon biscuits can be added with
the sponge cake.
   If whipping cream is available, use this in place of double cream as more
volume can be achieved.
   A layer of fresh soft fruit e.g. raspberries or sliced strawberries, which
may be macerated in a little sugar and cointreau or grand marnier, can be
used in place of jam.
   The egg custard can be given a chocolate flavour.
   The final decoration can include angelica or chocolate – grated, in curls
or in piped shapes.

A recipe for trifle (four portions)

• If using fresh vanilla pods to flavour milk for trifle, can the pods be
re-used and, if so, how are they kept?

....

• When cooking a fresh egg and milk mixture, why is it essential to
stir continuously and cook over a gentle heat?

....

- Why after cooking an eggs and milk mixture is it essential to strain the mixture through a fine strainer?

....

- Once an eggs and milk mixture has cooked and thickened, is it essential to remove it from the heat and, if so, why?

....

- If a cooked mixture of eggs and milk is removed from the heat and left in the pan without stirring, what will happen?

....

- Describe three variations of a fresh egg trifle.

....

....

....

3 Milk puddings and pastry cream (pp513–18, 530), *Practical Cookery*).
- What would be the effect of using wholemeal bread in place of white bread for a bread and butter pudding?
- How can the fat content of a bread and butter pudding be reduced?

....

- Why are the sultanas placed under rather than on top of the bread?

....

- What would be the effect of using two rather than three eggs to a pint of milk for bread and butter pudding?

....

- Why is it important to cook baked egg custard desserts in a bain-marie?

....

- What is the final addition to a baked egg custard before placing it in the oven?

....

- What is the oven setting for baked egg custard desserts?

....

- What is a cabinet pudding and how does it differ from a diplomat pudding?

....

- Suggest two sauces suitable for serving with cabinet pudding and two different sauces suitable for serving with diplomat pudding.

....

....

- Give a detailed description for the preparation of the caramel for a cream caramel.

....

....

....

- What will be the effect on flavour if the caramel is undercooked or overcooked?

....

- Give two reasons why it is necessary to add a quarter of the water after the caramel is cooked.

....

....

- What is the appropriate cooking time for cream caramels cooked at 160°C (mark 3)?

....

- When making pastry cream, after having whisked on the boiling milk to the remainder of the ingredients, why is it necessary to clean the pan before returning the mixture and completing the cooking?

....

- When pastry cream is removed into a container, how can the forming of a skin on top be prevented?

....

4 Hygiene.
- What are the main contamination threats when storing, preparing and cooking egg mixtures in relation to:

    1 Using the same preparation areas, equipment and utensils for preparing cooked and uncooked products:

....

    2 Using unhygienic equipment, utensils and preparation methods (support your answer with examples):

....

3 Touching the mouth, nose, open cuts, sores and unclean hands then handling food:

....

4 Uncovered foods and pests:

....

5 Incorrect disposal of waste:

....

6 Incorrect storage of unused items:

....

• Give four reasons why it is important to keep preparation and cooking areas and equipment hygienic.

....

....

....

....

5 Time and temperature are important when cooking egg-based desserts to ensure they are correctly cooked; to prevent food poisoning; and to minimise loss of nutritional value from prepared food.
• Give any examples where you have seen incorrect examples of the above three points.

....

....

....

6 Describe an egg custard based dessert which you have produced recently at college or at work. Give the number of portions prepared and comment on the quality. Did you consider it successful? Was there any way it could have been improved? Was there a way that you could suggest a variation? There is a full page for your answer overleaf.

....

....

....

....

....

UNIT 2D4 *Prepare and cook stocks, sauces and soups*

2D4.1 ## PREPARE AND COOK STOCKS

1 As stocks are the foundation of many important kitchen preparations, the greatest possible care should be taken in their production (p90, *Practical Cookery*).
a. Preparation and cooking areas and equipment before being used must satisfy health, safety and hygiene regulations.
b. Work should be planned and appropriate time allowed to meet daily schedules, e.g. if a stock takes six hours to cook, it is bad planning to start it three hours before the end of a day's work.
c. Ingredients are of the correct type, sound in quality and sufficient quantity.
d. Ingredients are correctly prepared and cooked according to the recipes.
e. Cooked stock, if not to be used immediately, is correctly and safely stored according to food hygiene legislation.
f. Preparation and cooking areas and equipment are correctly cleaned after use.
- Give two reasons why unsound meat or bones and decaying vegetables should not be used for stock.

....

....
- If scum is not removed during cooking it will boil into the stock and spoil the colour and ....
- If stock is allowed to boil rather than gently simmer, it will evaporate and ....
- What is the danger of allowing stock to go off the boil, particularly in hot weather?

....

....
- Why should salt not be added to stock?

....
- If stock is to be kept, there are four procedures to be carried out, straining, reboiling and

....

- When making chicken stock, if chicken carcasses are not available, what can be used as a substitute?

  ....

2 General methods for white and brown stocks (pp91–2, *Practical Cookery*).
- When chopping beef bones for stock, why is any fat or marrow removed and what safety precautions should be observed?

  ....

  ....

- To help keep a meat or game stock clean, blanching and refreshing is necessary. How is this done?

  ....

  ....

  ....

  ....

- Just before stock comes to the boil, if a good measure of cold water is added it will help to throw the scum and fat to the surface and ....
- What is the approximate cooking time for a beef stock?

  ....

- The three ingredients in a bouquet garni for beef stock are:

  ....

- The outside leaves of which vegetable are often used to enclose a bouquet garni?

  ....

- How could you describe a bouquet garni in English?

  ....

- To make a brown beef stock, the bones are browned well on all sides either by placing in a roasting tin in the oven or   .

  ....

- Before placing the browned bones in the stock pot, what must be done with them?

  ....

- Deglazing is an important procedure that follows the removal of the browned bones from the tray. What is the purpose of deglazing and how is it done?

....

....

....

....

- Why are the roughly chopped vegetables also coloured for brown stock?

....

- In addition to squashed (but sound) tomatoes, what other ingredient may be added to brown stock?

....

- If it takes 6–8 hours to extract the flavour from beef bones, how long should it take for a chicken stock made from raw carcasses: 1–2 hours, 1–4 hours or 5–6 hours? ....

3   Fish stock (p212, *Practical Cookery*).
- Why does fish stock only require 20 minutes cooking time?

....

- What would be the effect on the flavour of cooking fish stock for 1 hour?

....

- Why is it essential that fish bones used for stock are well washed and perfectly fresh?

....

4   Vegetarian stocks (p381, *Practical Cookery*).
- Four suitable vegetables for making vegetable stock are?

....

- What approximate length of cooking time is required for vegetable stock: $\frac{1}{2}$ hour, 1 hour, $1\frac{1}{2}$ hours or 2 hours? ....
- When making brown vegetable stock, why is it not suitable to colour off ingredients using lard or dripping?

....

- For what type of dishes are vegetable stocks used?

....

5   There are many possibilities of contamination when preparing cooking and storing stocks (read pp453–68 *Theory of Catering*).

a. If raw and cooked ingredients are *stored* together, e.g. cooked stock and raw bones or strong smelling vegetables.
b. Using the same preparation areas, equipment and utensils for preparing cooked and uncooked products.
• Give examples.

....

....

c. Unhygienic equipment, utensils and preparation methods, e.g. dirty ladle used for freshly made stock.
• Give another example.

....

d. Transfer of food poisoning bacteria from the mouth, nose, open cuts and sores and unclean hands to food.
• Give examples.

....

e. Incorrect waste disposal, e.g. after straining off a stock pot, leaving the remains lying uncovered for some time before disposing of them into a covered container.
• Give another example.

....

f. Incorrect storage of unused items, e.g. unused bones not placed in the correct refrigerator.
• Give another example.

....

g. Incorrect storage temperatures, e.g. cooked stock after being cooled not kept in the refrigerator or cold room.
h. Incorrect straining procedure, e.g. passing stock through a dirty strainer.
• Give another example.

....

6 Why is it important to keep preparation and cooking areas and equipment hygienic?
a. To prevent contamination of food by food poisoning bacteria, e.g. raw food being prepared on a work surface that was left improperly cleaned from the previous day.
• Give another example.

....

b. To prevent pest infestation and unpleasant odours from arising, e.g. rat droppings soon cause an unpleasant smell.
- Give another example.

....

c. To ensure that standards of cleanliness are maintained, e.g. clean hands and knives.
- Give another example.

....

d. To comply with the law, e.g. breaking the law can result in heavy fines.
- Give another example.

....

7 Time and temperature are important when cooking stocks.
a. To ensure a correctly cooked stock, e.g. sufficient time is required to extract maximum flavour from the ingredients.
- Give another example.

....

b. To prevent food poisoning, e.g. if stock is kept in a warm kitchen overnight rather than in a refrigerator it can go sour.
- Give another example.

....

c. To ensure that loss of nutritional value of prepared food is minimised, e.g. to rapidly chill stock, if it is to be kept, and to avoid keeping stock (if possible, make and use a stock as required).
8 Simmering stock pots for long periods is now considered bad practice. Many establishments do continue to make stocks, as a good stock is often an essential foundation to many culinary dishes. However, it is the policy of some establishments not to make stocks as a matter of hygiene policy.
- List the stocks you have prepared recently together with any commercial preparations you are either aware of or have used as a substitute.

....

....

....

....

2D4.2 | PREPARE AND COOK SAUCES

1   Sauces (pp92–110, *Practical Cookery*).

a.   Before commencing work ensure that all preparation and cooking areas and equipment are ready for use and satisfy health, safety and hygiene regulations.

b.   Check that work is planned and sufficient time allocated to meet daily schedules.

c.   All ingredients used for making sauces must be of the type, quality and quantity required.

d.   Ingredients must be correctly prepared and cooked according to the customer, dish and recipe requirements.

e.   Sauces must be correctly finished and presented according to customer and dish requirements.

f.   After use, all preparation and cooking areas and equipment must be correctly cleaned.

•   Name four ways of thickening liquid to form a sauce and give an example for each.

Thickening	*Sauce example*	*Dish for which sauce is suitable*
1 roux	béchamel/mornay	poached eggs Florentine
2		
3		
4		

2   When making a sauce the thickening medium should be used in moderation to give a light texture, and not a thick, unpalatable cloying mixture.

•   All sauces should be smooth, but how should they look and taste?

....

•   When making a roux-based sauce, a boiling liquid should never be added to a hot roux because the result may be lumpy, and what else?

•   What are the three degrees to which a roux can be cooked?

Roux	Example of a liquid	Sauce
1		
2		
3 blond	white chicken stock	suprême sauce

- In addition to butter or margarine, which other ingredient can be used to mix with flour? ....
- What is the benefit of using a slack rather than tight roux when incorporating the liquid?

....

- If a brown roux is overcooked, the starch in the flour will lose some of its thickening property owing to a chemical change known as *dextrinisation*. One effect of this is that the fat will separate from the roux and rise to the surface of the sauce.
- Give two other effects of dextrinisation.

....

....

- Name four sauces that can be made from béchamel and describe a dish with which each could be served.

Sauce	Dish
1 anchovy	breadcrumbed fried fillets of plaice, anchovy sauce
2	
3	
4 mustard	grilled herring, mustard sauce

- What two additions are made to béchamel for mornay sauce?

....

....

- How are onions cooked for addition to onion sauce?

....

- What are three alternative additions for finishing a cream sauce?

....

....

....

- Why are alternatives to cream sometimes used?

....

- Is English mustard always used to make mustard sauce, and if the answer is false, what is or are the alternative(s)? ....

- Name three starches used for thickening sauces.

....

- What are the three stages in thickening a starch-based sauce?

....

....

....

- When finishing a thickened gravy the best starch to use is arrowroot because it gives a completely clear finish to the gravy. As arrowroot is expensive, what substitute can be used?

....

- With what two roast joints is thickened gravy sometimes to be served? ....

- Is it essential to use a reduction when making a Hollandaise sauce? If not, why not, and what alternative can be used?

....

- How many egg yolks are used to make Hollandaise sauce from $\frac{1}{2}$ lb (200 g) butter: 1, 2, 3 or 4 egg yolks? ....

- Why is it essential to cook the yolks for an egg-based sauce over gentle heat and to continually whisk them?

....

- What is the name given to the stage to which yolks are cooked for an egg-based sauce?

....

- Why should an egg-based sauce not be served in a hot sauce boat?

....

- What are two reasons why an egg-based sauce will curdle?

....

- The effect of excess heat will cause the eggs to: ....
....

What are two ways of reconstituting a curdled sauce?

....

....

- What are the four ingredients used in the reduction for a béarnaise sauce?

....

....

- Other than additional flavours, what is the difference between a Hollandaise and béarnaise sauce?

....

3 In order to reduce the risk of salmonella infection when making egg-based sauces, pasteurised egg yolks may be used. As a further precaution, the warm sauce should then be discarded after it has been kept in a warm kitchen for more than two hours.
- Name two fish and two vegetables with which Hollandaise sauce may be served.

....

....

4 Roasting (p248, *Practical Cookery*).
- Why is it important to keep the sediment in the tray when making roast gravy?

....

- What is this sediment and where does it come from?

....

- Why is it important to strain off carefully the fat in the roasting tray after the meat or poultry joint is cooked and removed from the tray?

....

- When roasting a joint of beef, what accompaniment should the strained off beef fat be used for?

....

- What is the reason for carefully browning the sediment in the roasting tray before deglazing with stock?

....

- When roasting poultry, the procedure for making roast gravy is the same as for meat, with the exception of the stock which should be made from the bones and cleaned giblets of the poultry. What are giblets?

....

4 For vegetable gravy, white or brown vegetable stock can be used (p381, *Practical Cookery*) and lightly thickened with a starch if necessary. If vegetables are cooked in lightly salted water, then the liquid can also be used as a base for vegetable stock.

5 The main contamination threats when preparing, cooking and storing sauces are:

a. The transfer of food poisoning bacteria between cooked sauces and gravies and uncooked raw ingredients kept in the same store, larder or refrigerator, e.g. peeled onions kept in the same store as gravy.

- Give another example.

....

b. The transfer of food poisoning bacteria by using the same preparation areas, equipment and utensils for preparing cooked and uncooked sauces and gravies, e.g. cutting up vegetables on the same surface which had previously been used for cutting raw meat or poultry and not washed in between.

- Give another example.

....

c. The transfer of food poisoning bacteria from unhygienic equipment, utensils and preparation methods, e.g. cooking stock in a pan previously used for making a milk-based sauce which had not been properly cleaned.

- Give another example.

....

d. The transfer of food poisoning bacteria from the mouth, nose, open cuts and sores and unclean hands to food, e.g. smoking whilst cutting up food instead of leaving the kitchen for a smoke during a coffee break and then washing the hands before re-commencing work.

e. Uncovered food contaminated by pests carrying bacteria (p466, *Theory of Catering*).

- Give two examples.

....

f. Not disposing of waste or storing unused items in the correct

manner, e.g. if sauces or gravies are to be kept overnight, not cooling them and storing in a warm room instead of a refrigerator.
- Give another example.

....

6   Preparation, cooking and storage areas (see pp447–52 *Theory of Catering*).
7   Time and temperature are important when cooking sauces and gravies to ensure a correctly cooked sauce; to prevent food poisoning; and to ensure that loss of nutritional value of prepared food is minimised.
8   List the sauces you feel you are competent in producing. Write down examples of the dishes you have produced a sauce for (where possible write the dates). Show the list to your tutor. For example, supreme sauce: poached chicken and rice (produced in the main public restaurant on Tuesday 2 March, during the lunch period. Twenty-two customers in restaurant). These examples can also be used as evidence in candidate's achievement logbooks.

....

....

....

2D4.3 PREPARE AND COOK SOUPS

1   Before any preparation, cooking, finishing and serving soups the following points must be borne in mind:
a.   Preparation and cooking areas and equipment are ready for use and satisfy health, safety and hygiene regulations.
b.   Work is planned and time allocated to meet daily schedules.
c.   Ingredients for soups are of the type, quality and quantity required.
d.   Ingredients are prepared and cooked according to customer and recipe requirements.
e.   Soups are correctly finished and presented according to customer and dish requirements.
f.   Preparation, cooking areas and equipment are cleaned after use.
2   Cream soups (pp160–6, *Practical Cookery*).
- When finishing tomato soup to make it cream of tomato soup, reboil the finished soup, add $\frac{1}{2}$ pint milk and what two other ingredients? ....
- Suggest two variations to cream of tomato soup and name each.

....

- When making cream of tomato soup using fresh tomatoes, the colour may be rather pale. How can this be remedied?

....

- When making cream of mushroom soup, which of the following stocks would be used and why: beef, lamb, chicken, or veal?

....

- Why is it necessary to remove the bouquet garni before straining a cream soup?

....

....

- Traditionally, a cream soup is finished with fresh cream. If the fat content of the soup is required to be reduced, natural yoghurt can be used in place of cream. Name two other products which can be used in place of yogurt. ....

- The final consistency of cream soup should be smooth and just of sufficient thickness to lightly coat the back of a spoon. True or false? ....

- Leek and celery are suitable vegetables for use in a cream of vegetable soup. Name three other vegetables.

....

- What is an alternative to using all stock for the liquid when making a cream soup? ....

- Why is it suitable to use wholemeal flour in place of white flour for cream of vegetable soup, but not for cream of chicken soup?

....

- When making a cream of vegetable soup, what is the quantity of prepared vegetables required to 2 pints of stock: 4 ozs (100 g), 8 ozs (200 g), 12 ozs (300 g), or 1 lb (400 g)? ....

- Name six different kinds of creamed vegetable soup.

....

....

....

- Cream of asparagus soup is economic to make when asparagus is in full season as only the stalks which would otherwise be thrown away are used. True or false? ....

- Which stock would you use for making cream of asparagus soup and why? ....

3 Broth (pp155–6, *Practical Cookery*).

- A broth is a well-flavoured meat or poultry stock cooked together with a good quantity of neatly cut vegetables and garnished with dice of the meat or poultry and a cereal. True or false? ....

- What is the basic difference between Scotch and mutton broth?

....

- What are the cereals used to garnish the following broths?
  Scotch: ....
  mutton: ....
  chicken: ....

- When using a fresh piece of meat for mutton broth, why is it essential to blanch and refresh the meat and set it to cook in a clean pan?

....

- What is the approximate cooking time for barley: 15 min., 30 min., 45 min. or 1 hour? ....

- When making mutton broth, why is it not suitable to cook the meat, barley and vegetables together from the start?

....

- From the following list of vegetables, select four most suitable for a broth: onions, peas, beans, carrots, cabbage, leeks, turnips, celery.

....

- Finally, before serving, a broth is usually finished with chopped ....

- If a boiling fowl is not available to make chicken broth, would 4–6 chicken carcasses be suitable? ....

4 Purée soups (pp156–9, 162–6, *Practical Cookery*) are made from vegetables, generally with one vegetable dominating, flavoured with herbs and sometimes a little meat, e.g. ham or bacon. They can be made using stock or water, and the thickening agent is solely the vegetables when the soups are made from pulses, e.g. dried peas, beans and lentils. In other cases, if butter, margarine or oil is used to initially sweat the vegetables, then a little flour may be added to absorb the fat. Fried croutons accompany some purée soups, but if fat reduction is required, they may be toasted.

- When making a purée soup using green, yellow split or whole peas, it may be necessary to soak them overnight. True or false? ....

- Why may it be necessary to soak pulses overnight?

....

- Bouquet garni and knuckle of ham or bacon (optional) are usually added to a pulse soup. Name four other ingredients.

  ....

  ....

- What is the usual accompaniment to purée soups made from pulses?

  ....

- When making lentil soup it is not necessary to soak the lentils overnight. True or false? ....

- Select five vegetables suitable for using in a mixed vegetable soup: onion, aubergine, tomato, cauliflower, marrow, carrot, mange tout, leek, spinach, carrot. ....

- What are suitable garnishes for the following purée soups: cauliflower, celery, leek, and potato and watercress.

  ....

  ....

- What extra ingredient may be added to purée of lentil and carrot soups to enrich the colour? ....

5 It is essential to know and understand the main contamination threats when preparing, cooking and storing soups (see pp63–5).

6 Time and temperature are important when cooking soups to ensure a correctly cooked soup; to prevent food poisoning; and to ensure that loss of nutritional value of prepared food is minimised.

UNIT 2D5 *Prepare and cook pulse dishes*

2D5.1 1 Pulses are the dried seeds of plants which form pods, e.g. peas, beans, pp159–60, *The Theory of Catering*. Pulses are a popular versatile food, which with combinations of herbs, spices and vegetables, can be produced into many interesting dishes covering almost every course on the menu. Because pulses are good sources of protein and carbohydrate, they help to provide the body with energy and, with the single exception of the soya bean, they are completely deficient in fat. Non-meat eaters find them an important source of protein, and as they also have a high-fibre content this makes them particularly popular with those following a healthy diet.

2 Before starting any work with pulses the following points must be observed:

a. Preparation and cooking areas and equipment are ready for use and satisfy health, safety and hygiene regulations.

b. Work is planned and sufficient time allocated to meet daily schedules.

c. All ingredients used in recipes are of the correct type, quantity and quality.

d. Pulses are correctly prepared according to the recipes.

e. Pulses are correctly combined with other ingredients according to customer and dish requirements.

f. Pulse dishes are cooked, finished and presented according to customer and dish requirements.

g. All preparation and cooking areas and equipment are correctly cleaned after use.

3 Some pulses require pre-soaking before cooking, the soaking time varying considerably according to the type and quality of the pulses and the length of time they have been stored. For soaking, pulses should be comfortably covered in cold water and kept in a cold place. After soaking they should be washed and set to cook in fresh water.

Red kidney beans *must* always be soaked, washed off and boiled for at least 10 minutes – they contain a substance which unless 'killed' by adequate cooking, can lead to poisoning.

Salt should not be added to pulses before cooking as this will cause the pulse to toughen. Salt should be added as the pulse is almost cooked.

• Name the number of dishes prepared from pulses that you know.

....

....

....

....

• If a bowl of dried beans is to be soaked overnight, where is the most suitable place for them to be kept?

....

Read the following recipes in *Practical Cookery*: recipes 57, 58, p137; recipes 16–19, p156–7; recipe 5, p382; recipe 12, p387; recipe 15,

p388; recipe 20, p391; recipe 34, p402.
* Make a list of pulse dishes that can be cooked by the following methods:

stewing or casseroling	
grilling or barbecuing	
baking shallow or stir-frying	

* Name three dried beans suitable for making into three bean salad and give a reason for your choice.

* Name three pulses suitable for making into soup.

* List the ingredients and method for a burger recipe use a pulse in place of meat.

* Bean goulash is an example of a pulse dish cooked by stewing or in a casserole. Name one other method of stewing beans.

* Page 388, *Practical Cookery*, shows a recipe for a baked pulse dish. Suggest three ways which the recipe could be varied.

* In the Mexican bean pot recipe on p391, *Practical Cookery*, what

alternatives could you suggest for the following ingredients?
tomatoes, skinned, de-seeded and diced: ....
dried marjoram: ....
chopped chives: ....

- In the spiced chick peas recipe on p402, *Practical Cookery*, what is garam masala and what is its purpose in the recipe?

....

4 The main contamination threats when preparing and cooking pulse dishes are:

a. The transfer of food poisoning bacteria by using the same preparation areas, equipment and utensils for both cooked and uncooked products, e.g. using the same spoon for stirring hot pulse cooking and mixing a pulse salad.
- Give another example.

....

b. The transfer of food poisoning bacteria from unhygienic equipment, utensils and preparation methods, e.g. storing cooked pulses in a container that previously contained meat and that had been wiped out instead of properly washed.
c. The transfer of food poisoning bacteria from the mouth, nose, open cuts and sores and unclean hands to food, e.g. absent-mindedly scratching a sore on the arm and then without washing the hands, using them to mix a large quantity of pulse salad.
- Give another example.

....

d. Uncovered food contaminated by pests carrying bacteria (pp463–5, *The Theory of Catering*).
- Give an example from your experience.

....

e. Incorrect disposal for waste or storing unused items, e.g. leaving a bowl of cooked pulse uncovered in a warm room overnight.
- Give another example.

....

f. Contamination from unclean pulses. Pulses should always be carefully picked over to look for any foreign bodies before being used, e.g. one or two unsound beans could be sufficient to contaminate a large quantity.
5 Preparation and cooking areas and equipment must be kept hygienic at all times (see p82, pp447–52 *Theory of Catering*).

6   Time and temperature are important when cooking pulse dishes, otherwise the pulse recipe will be improperly cooked; to prevent food poisoning, and to ensure that any loss of nutritional value of prepared food is minimised.

7   Write down a recipe of your choice suitable for vegetarians using one or two different pulses.

8   Name and describe two different salads using pulses.

....

....

....

....

....

....

....

....

....

....

....

....

....

....

....

....

....

....

....

....

....

....

....

....

UNIT 2D6 *Prepare and cook fresh pasta*

2D6.1 **PREPARE AND COOK FRESH PASTA**

Read pp192–8, *Practical Cookery*, and p171, *The Theory of Catering*.

1 Before making and cooking pasta ensure that:

a. Preparation areas and equipment are ready for use and satisfy health, safety and hygiene regulations.

b. Work is planned and appropriate time allocated to meet daily schedules.

c. Ingredients are of the type, quality and quantity required.

d. Pasta is correctly prepared according to the dish requirements.

e. Prepared pasta not for immediate use is stored in accordance with food hygiene regulations, e.g. if fresh eggs are used in the making of fresh pasta, the fresher they are the longer the keeping quality of the pasta. When freshly made pasta is made for storage, it should be allowed to dry and be kept in a clean, dry container or bowl in a cool, dry store.

f. Pasta is correctly combined with other ingredients according to customer and dish requirements.

g. Pasta dishes are cooked and finished according to customer and dish requirements.

h. Preparation areas and equipment are correctly cleaned after use.

2 Recipes (recipes for noodle pasta and ravioli/cannelloni pasta are given on pp196, 197, *Practical Cookery*).

a. Fresh egg pasta dough   4 size 3 eggs, beaten
400 g (1 lb) strong flour   oil as required
salt

1 Sieve flour and salt, shape into a well.

2 Pour eggs into the well.

3 Gradually incorporate the flour and only add the oil if required to adjust the consistency. The amount of oil will vary according to the type of flour and size of the eggs.

4 Pull and knead the dough until it is of a smooth, elastic consistency.

5 Cover the dough with a dampened cloth and allow to rest in a cool place for 30 minutes.

6 Roll out the dough on a well-floured surface until $\frac{1}{4}$ cm (1/8 in) thick, or use a pasta rolling machine (see note on page 80).

7 Trim the sides and cut the dough as required using a large knife.

Note: If using a pasta rolling machine, divide the dough into three to four pieces. Pass each section by hand through the machine turning the rollers with the other hand. Repeat this five to six times.

b. Green pasta: add 75–100 g (3–4 oz) finely puréed, dry, cooked spinach to the dough.

c. Red pasta: add 2 tablespoons of tomato purée to the dough.

d. Wholewheat pasta: use half white and half wholemeal flour.

e. Filled pasta: raviolis and cannellonis are two of the most popular types of stuffed pasta, but there are many other forms and a wide variety of fillings. Examples of fillings:

minced cooked meat	chopped fish
spinach	chopped mushrooms
onion, garlic	chopped parsley
oregano, salt, pepper	anchovy paste
ricotta cheese	aubergine, peeled, cubed and deep fried
spinach	walnuts, shelled and chopped
nutmeg, salt, pepper	chopped parsley
egg yolks	thick béchamel

• Always cook pasta in plenty of gently boiling salted water. Name the three other general points on the cooking and serving of pasta.

....

....

....

• What does the term *al dente* mean?

....

• Which cheese is traditionally served with pasta dishes?

....

• If wholewheat noodles are required, what proportion of wholewheat flour is added to the basic dough?

....

• Why after making pasta dough is it necessary to allow it to rest and relax?

....

• What spice may be used in a dish of buttered noodles?

....

- What is the approximate cooking time for meat ravioli: 5 min., 10 min. or 15 min.? ....
- Name two sauces that could be served with meat ravioli.

....

- Other than the shape, what is the basic difference in the handling and cooking of pasta for ravioli and cannelloni?

....

- Name three types of pasta sheets that can be used in the making of a lasagne.

....

- Write out your idea for a non-meat lasagne.

....

....

....

....

- The number of pasta shapes available exceeds: 10, 20, 30, 40 or 50 shapes? ....
3 The main contamination threats when preparing, cooking and storing pasta (pp453–68, *The Theory of Catering*).
a. The transfer of food poisoning bacteria by using the same preparation areas, equipment and utensils for preparing cooked and uncooked products.
- Give an example.

....

b. The transfer of food poisoning bacteria from unhygienic equipment, utensils and preparation methods.
- Give an example.

....

c. The transfer of food poisoning bacteria from the mouth, nose, open cuts and sores and unclean hands to food.
- Give an example.

....

d. Uncovered food contaminated by pests carrying bacteria.
- Give an example.

....

e. Not disposing of waste or storing unused items in the correct manner.

- Give an example.

....

4   It is important to keep preparation and storage areas and equipment hygienic.
a. To prevent contamination of food by food poisoning bacteria.
- Give an example.

....

b. To prevent pest infestation and unpleasant odours arising.
- Give an example.

....

c. To ensure that standards of cleanliness are maintained.
- Give an example.

....

d. To comply with the law.
- Give an example.

....

5   Time and temperature are important in the cooking of fresh pasta:
a. To ensure correctly cooked pasta and pasta dishes, e.g. if pasta, such as noodles and spaghetti, are not cooked in ample gently boiling water they will clog together; and if pasta is overcooked it will become soft and mushy.
- To what degree should pasta be cooked?

....

b. To prevent food poisoning, e.g. if undercooked fresh egg pasta is allowed to remain warm in a warm kitchen for a considerable period of time food poisoning bacteria could multiply.
c. To ensure that the loss of nutritional value of prepared food is minimised, e.g. keeping prepared food warm for long periods will result in nutritional loss, therefore reheat pasta and combine the ingredients quickly and serve immediately.
d. Prepared cooked pasta may also be kept in a vacuum pack and stored under refrigeration for several days.
6   Draw several different pasta shapes that you have recently cooked and served. Under each shape give its name and a menu example.

UNIT 2D7 *Prepare and cook dough products*

PREPARE DOUGH PRODUCTS FOR COOKING

1   Dough is kneaded, moistened flour. Before commencing any dough preparation the following points must be observed:

a. Preparation areas and equipment are ready for use and satisfy health, safety and hygiene regulations.

b. Work is planned and time appropriately allocated to meet daily schedules.

c. Dough ingredients, (flour, yeast, etc.) are of the type, quality and quantity required.

d. Dough is prepared according to product requirements.

e. Prepared dough is stored in accordance with food hygiene regulations.

f. Preparation areas and equipment are correctly cleaned after use.

2   Yeast (pp145–6, *The Theory of Catering*).

•   Complete the following six quality and storage points for fresh yeast:

Yeast should be wrapped and stored in ....

It should be ordered only ....

It must be perfectly .... and ....

The smell must be ....

Yeast should .... easily.

The colour of yeast is ....

(Yeast is also available as a dried product, which if kept in sealed containers has a much longer life than fresh yeast.)

•   As dried yeast has been dehydrated, what has to be done with it to make it ready for use?

....

•   Complete the following seven important points to remember when using yeast:

Yeast should be removed from the refrigerator and used at .... temperature.

What is the effect of salt on the working of yeast? ....

The more salt used, the .... the action of the yeast.

The best temperature for yeast action is ....

The best temperature for liquid for mixing dough is ....

Temperatures over .... can destroy yeast and make any subsequent dough unusable.

Yeast can sustain .... temperatures without damage.

- What do you understand by the terms kneading and proving?

....

....

- What is meant by overproving?

....

- What are the causes of overproving?

....

3 Yeast dough (pp470–3, *Practical Cookery*).
- Why is the flour warmed before making a yeast dough?

....

- What is the first stage in using yeast before adding to the flour?

....

- When the yeast mixture is added to the flour and sprinkled with a little flour, the bowl is covered with a cloth and left in a warm place. What process takes place next? ....
- Complete the following to test your underpinning knowledge. When the remainder of the ingredients for the dough are added the kneading process takes place, which means initially mixing, then working the dough firmly with both hands on a lightly floured surface until .... and free from ....? Pushing the dough out into a thick strip and folding it can be part of this process. After the dough has been kneaded, it is returned to the basin, covered with a cloth and left in a warm place until it has doubled in size. This is known as ....?
- After the dough has .... it is then knocked back, which means expelling all the air by firm use of both hands.

  The dough is now ready to be moulded into the desired shape(s) and sizes. Bread rolls can be shaped in a variety of ways (p471, *Practical Cookery*). The dough is initially divided into even-sized pieces to ensure the rolls are of the same size.

  Plaiting: the piece of dough is shaped into three equal thick lengths which are then laid side by side; start interlacing from the centre working out to each end.

After the dough has been moulded into the desired shape, it is either placed on a greased baking sheet (rolls) or into greased bread tins covered with a cloth and left to double in size. Finally, the dough products may be carefully brushed with egg wash and are ready for the oven.

* What is egg wash? ....
* What is its purpose? ....
* What is this process called? ....
* What would happen if you brushed the proven dough too firmly?

....

* To make a wholemeal or wheatmeal dough, what is used in place of white flour?

....

* To make basic bun dough, three extra ingredients are added to flour, milk and water and yeast. What are these?

....

* Are these extra ingredients added to the bun dough before or after the yeast has fermented? ....
* What are the signs that show the yeast has fermented?

....

4   The main contamination threats when preparing and cooking dough products.

a. The transfer of food poisoning bacteria by using the same preparation areas, equipment and utensils for preparing cooked and uncooked products.
* Give an example.

....

b. The transfer of food poisoning bacteria from unhygienic equipment, utensils and preparation methods.
* Give an example.

....

c. The transfer of food poisoning bacteria from the mouth, nose, open cuts and sores and unclean hands to food.
* Give an example.

....

d. Uncovered food contaminated by pests carrying bacteria.
- Give an example.

....

e. Not disposing of waste or storing unused items in the correct manner.
- Give an example.

....

5 Keeping preparation and cooking areas and equipment hygienic.
a. To prevent contamination of food by food poisoning bacteria.
- Give an example.

....

b. To prevent pest infestation and unpleasant smells.
- Give an example.

....

c. To ensure standards of cleanliness are maintained.
- Give an example.

....

d. To comply with the law.
- Give an example.

....

6 Time and temperature are vitally important in the preparation of dough products.
- Give two reasons why.

....

....

As yeast is a form of plant life (fungus) consisting of minute cells, these cells grow and multiply at blood heat provided they are fed with sugar and liquid. The sugar causes the fermentation which is the production of gas (carbon dioxide) and alcohol in the form of small bubbles in the dough. When warmth is applied, the dough rises. The timing of this process has to be co-ordinated with temperature.
- Without correct application of time and temperature, the dough products will not be .... for the cooking process.

2D7.2 COOK DOUGH PRODUCTS

1 Basic rules for cooking any dough products:

a. Cooking areas and equipment must be ready for use and satisfy health, safety and hygiene regulations.
b. Work is planned and time appropriately allocated to meet daily schedules.
c. Dough is suitably prepared for the cooking process.
d. Dough is cooked according to product requirements.
e. Cooked dough products are finished according to product requirements.
f. Finished dough products are stored in accordance with food hygiene regulations.
g. Preparation and cooking areas are correctly cleaned after use.
2 Bread loaves can be made in many shapes and sizes, and either cooked in bread tin moulds or free standing on baking sheets. The following recipe will make two 400 g (1 lb) loaves:

White bread
500 g (1¼ lb) strong flour
10 g (½ oz) salt
10 g (½ oz) lard
30 g (1½ oz) yeast
300 ml (12 fl oz) water (at 45°C)
10 g (½ oz) sugar

1 Sieve the flour and salt into a warmed bowl.
2 Dissolve the yeast and sugar in the water.
3 Mix into the flour to form a soft dough.
4 Knead the dough thoroughly, place in a bowl and cover with a cloth.
5 Allow to prove until double in size (approx 1 hour).
6 Knead the dough, divide it into two, mould it and place in greased bread tins.
7 Allow to prove until double in size.
8 Bake at 200°C (400°F) for 30–45 minutes.

Wholemeal bread: as for white bread using 450 g (18 oz) wholemeal flour and 50 g (2 oz) strong white flour.

To test when the bread loaves are cooked, turn them upside down and tap their bottoms sharply with the knuckles. The loaves should sound hollow to indicate that they have lost much of their moisture during baking. (For bread rolls, see pp471–2, *Practical Cookery*.)
• Why is the flour and liquid used warm when making bread dough?

- Why is it necessary for the yeast to ferment before mixing it into the dough?

....

- When kneading bread dough, what is the sign that indicates it has been sufficiently kneaded?

....

- When a dough is sufficiently proved, how large should it be?

....

- What will be the effect of extreme heat on the yeast at any stage of bread making and what will be the subsequent effect on the bread?

....

3 Recipes for bun dough, bun wash, fruit, hot-cross buns, Bath, Chelsea, Swiss buns and doughnuts can be found on pp472–4, *Practical Cookery.*
- The purpose of using bun wash on certain buns is to give them a glaze or shine. What are the ingredients in a bun wash and when should it be brushed on the buns?

....

- Swiss buns when cooked are not finished with bun wash, they are finished (iced) with what?

....

(Fruit buns are glazed with bun wash as soon as they are cooked, Swiss buns are left to cool before icing.)
- How many buns are obtained from a 200 g ($\frac{1}{2}$ lb) flour bun dough mix 4, 6, 8, 10 or 12? ....
- What is the frying temperature for doughnuts: 125°C, 150°C, 175°C or 200°C?

....

4 Hygiene (pp447–68 *Theory of Catering*).
- There are five main contamination threats when preparing and cooking dough products. Name them and give examples.

....

....

....

....

....

- It is important to keep preparation; cooking and storage areas and equipment hygienic for four good reasons. Name them.

....

....

....

....

5   Time and temperature are particularly important when cooking dough products, otherwise a correctly cooked product will not result.
- Name another reason.

....

6   List all the dough products you have made recently. With the aid of drawings, describe the finished items.

UNIT 2D8 *Prepare and cook pastry dishes*

2D8.1 PREPARE FRESH PASTRY

1 Always comply with the following points:

a. Preparation areas and equipment are ready for use and satisfy health, safety and hygiene regulations.

b. Work is planned and time appropriately allocated to meet daily schedules.

c. Pastry ingredients are of the type, quality and quantity required, e.g. correct types of flour, fats with no signs of rancidity, and fresh untainted eggs.

d. Pastry is prepared according to dish requirements.

e. Prepared pastry is stored in accordance with food hygiene regulations.

f. Preparation areas and equipment are correctly cleaned after use.

2 Pastry (pp457–61, *Practical Cookery*, and pp144–5, *The Theory of Catering*).

- What is the proportion of flour to fat for short pastry: 1–1, $1\frac{1}{2}$–1, 2–1, $2\frac{1}{2}$–1 or 3–1? ....

- Why is it important to sieve flour and salt before making pastry?

....

- Why is it an advantage to have cool hands when mixing short pastry?

....

- What is the flour content for wholemeal short pastry?

....

- Give three uses for short pastry.

....

- Give two reasons for each of the following faults in short pastry:
  hard: ....
  soft, crumbly: ....
  blistered: ....
  soggy: ....
  shrunken: ....

- What type of flour is used in making short and sweet pastry? ....
- What is the proportion of flour to fat when making sweet pastry: 1–1, 2–1, 3–1, 4–1, 4–2, or 4–2$\frac{1}{2}$? ....
- What are the two ingredients added to sweet pastry not used in short pastry? ....
- There are two methods of making sweet pastry, one is the creaming method, the other is ....
- Why is it necessary to rest sweet pastry before rolling?

....

- Where is the best place to rest sweet pastry? ....
- What is the flour difference when making wholemeal sweet pastry?

....

- Sweet pastry is also known as sugar pastry. True or false? ....
- Name three items made from sweet pastry?

....

- What type of flour is used in making puff pastry and why?

....

- What is the ratio of flour to fat for making puff pastry: 1–1, 1$\frac{1}{2}$–1, 2–1, 2$\frac{1}{2}$–1, 3–2 or 5–2? ....
- The reason for adding a little acid to puff pastry is to strengthen the gluten (p140, *The Theory of Catering*) which helps to make a stronger dough. Any one of three acids may be added: ascorbic acid, tartaric acid, and .... acid.
- Why is it important to make a strong dough for puff pastry?

....

- When placing the fat on the basic dough, it is important to ensure that the texture of the butter is the same as that of the dough. True or false? ....
- What would happen if a hard fat were folded into a soft dough?

....

- Describe one double turn of puff pastry and what must be done before making a further turn?

....

- Why is it necessary to rest puff pastry in a cool place between turns?

....

Where and when time permits, puff pastry can also be given single rather double turns. In this case, six single turns are given, two at a time with a 2–3 hour rest in a cool place in between each pair of turns. Ask your tutor or trainer to show you a single turn.

- Why when rolling out puff pastry for turning is it essential to keep the ends and sides square?

....

- Well-made puff pastry when baked should have a light flaky formation. What causes this flakiness?

....

- Cream horns and jam turnovers can be made from puff pastry. Name four other items.

....

....

- Give two reasons for each of the following faults in puff pastry?
  not flaky: ....
  fat oozes out: ....
  hard: ....
  shrunken: ....
  soggy: ....
  uneven rise: ....
- In between turns and when ready for use, puff pastry should be wrapped in a cloth or plastic and kept in a refrigerator. True or false? ....
- What is the difference in the flour to fat ratio between puff and rough puff pastry?

....

- What is the method of adding fat to flour when making rough puff pastry: rubbing in finely, creaming, rubbing in pieces, or folding in? ....
- Can wholemeal flour be used in making puff and rough puff pastry and, if so, in what proportion? ....
- What type of flour is used in making suet pastry? ....
- What is the raising agent used in suet pastry? ....
- What is the ratio of flour to fat for suet paste: 1–1, $1\frac{1}{2}$–1, 2–1, $2\frac{1}{2}$–1 or 3–1? ....
- Sufficient water should be used in making suet pastry to form a soft dough, firm dough or fairly stiff dough? ....

- Give a reason for the following faults in suet paste:
  heavy and soggy: ....
  tough: ....
- Name three dishes using suet pastry.

....

....

3 The main contamination threats when preparing and storing fresh pastry are:

a. The transfer of food poisoning bacteria by using the same preparation areas, equipment and utensils for preparing cooked and uncooked products, e.g. using a bowl in which eggs were beaten for storing pastry without properly cleaning and drying the bowl.

- Give another example.

....

b. The transfer of food poisoning bacteria from unhygienic equipment, utensils and preparation methods, e.g. sifting flour through a dirty sieve (the flour sieve should be kept in a clean drawer).

- Give another example.

....

c. The transfer of food poisoning bacteria from the mouth, nose, open cuts and sores and unclean hands to food, e.g. failing to wash the hands after going to the toilet and then rubbing pastry.

- Give another example.

....

d. Uncovered food contaminated by pests carrying bacteria, e.g. an uncovered flour bin can attract many hungry pests.

- Give another example.

....

e. Not disposing of waste or storing unused items in the correct manner, e.g. left over pastry left unwrapped and out of the refrigerator.

- Give another example.

....

4 Time and temperature are important when preparing fresh pastry because unless pastry is made quickly, particularly in a warm

kitchen, it will become too soft and difficult to handle.
- Give another example.

....

COOK PASTRY DISHES

1 Before starting work ensure that:

a. Preparation and cooking areas and equipment are ready for use and satisfy health, safety and hygiene regulations.

b. Work is planned and time appropriately allocated to meet daily schedules, e.g. unless sufficient time is allowed, tasks will not be carried out properly and results will be poor.

c. Pastry dishes are of the type, quality and quantity required.

d. Pastry is suitably prepared according to dish requirements.

e. Pastry is correctly combined with other ingredients according to customer and recipe requirements.

f. Pastry dishes are cooked according to customer and dish requirements.

g. Pastry dishes for immediate consumption are finished and presented according to customer and dish requirements.

h. Pastry dishes not for immediate consumption are stored in accordance with the food hygiene regulations.

i. Preparation and cooking areas and equipment are correctly cleaned after use.

2 Short pastry (recipes 44–7, pp477–8; recipes 55–6, p482; recipe 32, p259, *Practical Cookery*).

- Name three fruits suitable for fruit pies.

....

- Name three pairs of fruit suitable for fruit pies.

....

- All fruit for fruit pies should be washed. True or false? ....
- Name two spices that can be used to flavour an apple pie.

....

- When rolling out pastry for a fruit pie, is it important not to stretch it because if the pastry is stretched when rolled or laid out, when the pie is placed in a hot oven, the pastry will ....
- What is the purpose of brushing a fruit pie with milk and sprinkling with castor sugar before baking?

....

- At what temperature should a fruit pie be placed in the oven: 180°C, 200°C, 220°C, 240°C or 260°C? ....
- Name three suitable accompaniments for a fruit pie.

  ....

- What is the preparation required for the following fruits when being used for fruit pies?
  apples: ....
  rhubarb: ....
  gooseberries: ....

  Jam tarts can be made in individual tartlet moulds, on a plate or in a shallow flan ring. When the pastry has been moulded, the bottom should be pricked several times with a fork. This is to stop the pastry rising in the heat of the oven and pushing the jam over the edges.

- What thickness is pastry rolled out for jam tart: 1.5 mm ($\frac{1}{16}$ in), 3 mm ($\frac{1}{8}$ in) or 6 mm ($\frac{1}{4}$ in)? ....
- Four ingredients are used to make the filling for a treacle or syrup tart: syrup or treacle, lemon juice, water and ....
- The traditional filling for a Cornish pasty includes finely diced raw potato, thinly cut raw lamb or beef, chopped onion and ....?
- What diameter is short paste cut for Cornish pasties: 3 in, 4 in, 5 in, 6 in, 7 in or 8 in? ....
- Why is it important to egg wash the edges of the pastie before folding it in half?

  ....

- How is the edge of a pastie fluted? (Ask your tutor to show you if necessary.)

  ....

- Why is it necessary to cook Cornish pasties in a moderate rather than hot oven for $\frac{3}{4}$–1 hour?

  ....

- Cornish pasties may be served hot or cold. True or false? ....
- How are apples prepared for baked apple dumpling?

  ....

- How are apple dumplings finished and decorated by using pastry trimmings?

  ....

- What is an appropriate cooking time for baked apple dumplings at 200°C: 15 min., 30 min., 45 min. or 60 min.? ....
- Suggest a variation to a basic baked apple.

....

3   Sweet pastry (recipes 48–54, pp477–81; recipes 57–70, pp482–6; *Practical Cookery*).
- After making sweet pastry and before using, it should be allowed to rest in the refrigerator before rolling it out. This allows the pastry to relax and lessens the risk of it .... when cooking, and allows the pastry to firm up and make it easier to ....
- If the bottom of the flan or tartlet cases are not pricked with a fork while uncooked, what is likely to happen when they are cooking?

....

- What is the oven temperature required for baking a fresh fruit flan: 150–180°C, 200–230°C or 250–280°C? ....
- When should the flan ring be removed from a flan case and how can a shine be given to the sides?

....

- Describe the making, baking and finishing of an apple flan.

....

....

....

- When finishing a fruit flan by glazing it, the glaze, e.g. apricot, should be used hot. Why is this?

....

- In addition to grated lemon zest, what two ingredients are added to an apple tart when making Dutch apple tart? ....
- When making a rhubarb flan a layer of .... may be added before the fruit. Other fruit flans, such as gooseberry, plum and apricot, may also have a layer of .... added before the fruit.
- Name three flans for which the flan case is cooked blind.

....

- Why is a flan case lined and filled with baking beans when cooking blind?

....

- What is the difference between a fruit tartlet and a fruit barquet?

- When finishing a banana flan, why is it important to cover the sliced bananas with apricot glaze or flan glaze as quickly as possible?

4   Puff or rough puff pastry (recipes 71–84, pp487–94).
- When making cream horns after the pastry has been cut into strips, why is it important to moisten each strip on one side?

- When making cream horns, at which end of the moulds is the pastry strip first started? ....
- When many puff pastry goods are almost cooked they can be given an appetising, shiny finish by sprinkling with icing sugar and returning briefly to a hot oven. This has the effect of lightly caramelising the sugar, making it shine. What is this process called?

- After cream horns are baked and cooled, how are they finished before serving?

- What are the four ingredients for the filling for Eccles cakes?

- When making jam or apple turnovers, what will happen if too much jam or apple purée is used and the edges are not firmly sealed?

- What is the difference in the traditional shape of a jam turnover and a jam puff?

- Unless a good quality, carefully prepared and handled puff pastry is used for making puff pastry cases, then the cases will not be suitable for being filled. Why?

- Small puff pastry cases are known as ....
- Large puff pastry cases are known as ....
- After puff pastry cases are baked and cooled, what should be done to make them ready for use? ....

- Suggest two uses each for serving cold bouchées as pastries and two for serving hot as savouries?

....

....

- What thickness should puff or rough puff pastry be rolled for making sausage rolls: $\frac{1}{16}$ in, (2 mm) $\frac{1}{8}$ in, (4 mm) $\frac{1}{4}$ in or $\frac{1}{2}$ in (1.2 cm)? ....

- Mince pies can be made with puff or rough puff pastry; they can also be made using two other pastes. What are they?

....

5 Suet paste (recipe 5, p461; recipes 91–5, pp497–8; recipes 34–6, p285; recipe 46, p292, *Practical Cookery*).

- Name two suitable fillings for a fruit steamed suet pudding.

....

- Why is it essential to tightly cover a suet pudding to be steamed with either greased greaseproof paper, silicone paper, a pudding cloth or foil?

....

- Why should puddings only be placed in the steamer when the pressure gauge indicates that the required degree of temperature has been reached?

....

- What is meant in relation to steamed suet puddings by:
  moulding: ....
  traying-up: ....
  loading: ....

- Describe the making of a steamed jam roll.

....

....

....

....

- Name four dried fruits suitable for use in a steamed suet pudding.

....

- Name two sauces suitable for serving with a steamed golden syrup suet pudding.

....

- Name two variations for a steamed steak pudding.

....

- In addition to the meat content, what other seasonings may be added to a steamed pudding?

....

- What is the appropriate cooking time for a four portion meat pudding using raw meat: $1\frac{1}{2}$ hrs, $2\frac{1}{2}$ hrs, $3\frac{1}{2}$ hrs, $4\frac{1}{2}$ hrs or $5\frac{1}{2}$ hrs? ....
- How many dumplings can be made out of 100 g (4 oz) suet paste: 2, 4, 6, 8, 10, 12, 14 or 16? ....
- When and how are dumplings cooked in a dish of braised steak and dumplings?

....

6 The main contamination threats when preparing and cooking pastry dishes are:

a. The transfer of food poisoning bacteria by using the same preparation areas, equipment and utensils for preparing cooked and uncooked products, e.g. using same area for making sausage rolls and finished fresh cream cakes.

b. The transfer of food poisoning bacteria from unhygienic equipment, utensils and preparation methods, e.g. beating eggs in an unclean bowl using a dirty whisk.

c. The transfer of food poisoning bacteria from the mouth, nose, open cuts, and sores and unclean hands to food, e.g. rubbing in fat to flour using unwashed hands with long, dirty finger nails.

d. Uncovered food contaminated by pests carrying bacteria, e.g. small insects can easily get into flour if it is left uncovered.

e. Not disposing of waste or storing unused items in the correct manner, e.g. storing cream-filled pastries on an unprotected shelf without refrigeration.

7 It is important to keep preparation areas and equipment hygienic in order to:

a. Prevent contamination of food by food poisoning bacteria.

- Give and example.

....

b. Prevent prest infestation and unpleasant smells from arising, e.g. pests are particularly attracted to foods in the pastry areas because of their sweetness.

c. Ensure that standards of cleanliness are maintained, e.g. many items used in pastry work (whisks, mixing machines, etc.) are likely harbours for bacteria.

d. Comply with the law, e.g. failure to comply with the law can lead to a conviction and a subsequent heavy fine.

8 Time and temperature are important when cooking pastry:

a. To ensure correctly cooked pastry dishes.

• Give an example.

....

b. To ensure that loss of nutritional value of prepared food is minimised.

• Give an example.

....

8 List the pastry items you have recently prepared from the following:

a. Short pastry:

....

....

....

....

....

b. Sweet pastry:

....

....

....

....

c. Puff pastry:

....

....

....

....

....

9 Name the hygiene precautions taken by the pastry department you have recently worked in, e.g. all risk items stored at 3°C refrigerated separately.

UNIT 2D9 *Prepare, cook and decorate cakes and biscuits*

2D9.1 PREPARE CAKE AND BISCUIT MIXTURES

1 Before starting work it is important that:
a. Preparation areas, equipment are ready for use and satisfy health, safety and hygiene regulations.
b. Work is planned and time allocated to meet daily schedules.
c. Ingredients are of the type, quality and quantity required.
d. Mixtures are prepared according to product requirements.
e. Prepared mixtures are stored in accordance with food hygiene regulations.
f. Preparation areas and equipment are correctly cleaned after use.
2 Cakes (recipes 7–15, pp463–6; recipe 196, p532, *Practical Cookery*; p144, *The Theory of Catering*).
- Complete the following requirements for making light scones:
  1 The correct proportion of .... to flour.
  2 After rubbing-in fat to flour, when adding liquid mix to ....
  ....
  3 The comparatively small amount of ....
  4 Quick and .... handling.
- Cake mixtures containing baking powder should be baked as soon as they are mixed. True or false? ....
- The effect of over-use of baking powder in cakes is that: they will have a .... taste, and they will .... in the middle.
- The effect of under-use of baking powder is that: the cake textures will be ....
  Therefore, baking powder must always be carefully and accurately measured before being used.
- What adjustments are required to the basic scone mix to make wholemeal scones and fruit scones?

....

- Describe each method for making a basic small cake mixture.
  1 Rubbing in:

....

....

....

....

2 Creaming:

....

....

....

....

- What is the difference in technique when adding the beaten eggs to each method?
  1 Rubbing:

....

....

2 Creaming:

....

....

- Irrespective of which method used, what is the correct consistency for the mixture?

....

- What is the alternative to using flour and baking powder?

....

- What type of flour is used for small cakes? ....
- There are six possible reasons for faults in cakes. Give one more reason for each fault.

  1 Uneven   (a) fat insufficiently rubbing in
    texture: (b) too little liquid
                 (c) ....

  2 Close texture: (a) hands too hot when rubbing in
                 (b) too much fat
                 (c) ....

  3 Dry: (a) oven too hot
                 (b) ....

  4 Bad shape: (a) too much liquid
                 (b) too much baking powder
                 (c) ....

  5 Fruit sunk: (a) fruit wet
                 (b) too much liquid

6 Cracked: (a) too much baking powder
                 (b) ....

- What two extra ingredients are added to the basic mixture to make cherry cakes?

....

....

- What two extra ingredients are added to the basic mixture for making coconut cakes?

....

- The flour and flavouring adjustments for making coconut cakes are, vanilla essence, and ....
- Describe the making of raspberry buns.

....

....

....

....

- Queen cakes are made from the basic small cake mixture with the addition of 100 g (4 oz) washed and dried mixed fruit. True or false? ....
- What fruit would be used in Queen cakes?

....

- When making a large fruit cake, the fat and sugar are: creamed until soft and ....; and the beaten eggs are added .... and .... in between.
- What is the advantage of using silicone over greaseproof paper for lining cake tins?

....

3 Sponges (recipes 16–22, pp466–9, *Practical Cookery*).
- There are five possible reasons for faults in sponges. Give another reason in each case:
  1 Close texture: (a) underbeating
                    (b) oven too cool or too hot
                    (c) ....
  2 Holey texture: (a) flour insufficiently folded in
                    (b) ....
  3 Cracked crust: (a) ....

4 Sunken: (a) tin removed during baking

(b) ....

5 White spots on surface:

- Give the proportion of ingredients for a Victoria sponge sandwich.
Butter or margarine: .... Flour: ....
Castor sugar: .... Eggs: ....
- What type of flour is used for a Victoria sponge? ....
- What is the basic difference between making a Victoria sponge and a Genoese sponge?

....

- The basic principle of making a Genoese sponge is to form the lightest, aerated mixture of eggs and sugar. Why then is it essential that both the flour and melted butter be added as carefully and gently as possible?

....

- Give one other reason for faults in Genoese sponges.
  1 Close texture: (a) too much flour
      (b) eggs and sugar over or under-beaten
      (c) ....
  2 Sunken: (a) too much sugar
      (b) oven too hot
      (c) ....
  3 Heavy: (a) butter too hot
      (b) Butter insufficiently mixed in
      (c) ....
- What is the name given to the beaten eggs and sugar when they have reached the final stage and are ready for the flour to be folded in? ....
- What is the method of preparing a mould for a Genoese sponge?

....

- What variation is required from the basic recipe to make a chocolate Genoese sponge? ....

....

- What type of flour is used for Genoese sponge?
- The basic method of making sponge for a Swiss roll is the same as for Genoese sponge. True or false? ....

4 Biscuits (recipes 201–5, pp534–6; recipe 23, p469; *Practical Cookery*).

- When making cats tongues biscuits, after the initial creaming of sugar and butter, it is necessary to add the egg whites one by one continually mixing. What would happen if the egg whites were added too quickly and the mixture was insufficiently beaten?

....

....

- When adding the flour to the cats tongues biscuit mixture it must be gently and lightly folded in. If the flour were whisked in quickly, what would the resulting biscuits be like?

....

- When piping out cats tongues biscuits they must be $2\frac{1}{2}$ cm (1 in) apart. Why is this necessary?

....

- What is the name of the biscuit made using the same mixture as for cats tongues but piped into rounds? ....
- When making sablé biscuits, what type of piping tube is used and in to what shape are they piped?

....

- Name three items that can be used to decorate sablé biscuits.

....

- On to what type of paper are almond biscuits piped and why?

....

- A simple shortbread biscuit recipe is (add the ingredients in each case):
  150 g (6 oz) ....   50 g (2 oz) ....
  100 g (4 oz) ....   pinch of salt ....
- When the shortbread biscuit mix is shaped and placed on a lightly greased baking sheet, it is pricked with a fork and marked with a knife into the required size and shapes. Why is it important to do this before baking?

....

5   The main contamination threats when preparing and storing raw cake and biscuit mixtures are:

a. The transfer of food poisoning bacteria by using the same preparation areas, equipment and utensils for preparing cooked and uncooked products.

- Give an example.

....

b. The transfer of food poisoning bacteria from unhygienic equipment, utensils and preparation methods.
- Give an example.

....

c. The transfer of food poisoning bacteria from the mouth, nose, open cuts and sores and unclean hands to food.
- Give an example.

....

d. Uncovered food contaminated by pests carrying bacteria.
- Give an example.

....

e. Not disposing of waste or storing unused items in the correct manner.
- Give an example.

....

6 It is important to keep preparation and storage areas and equipment hygienic in order to:
a. Prevent contamination of food by food poisoning bacteria.
- Give an example.

....

b. Prevent pest infestation and unpleasant odours arising.
- Give an example.

....

c. Ensure that standards of cleanliness are maintained.
- Give an example.

....

d. Comply with the law.
- Give an example.

....

2D9.2 COOK CAKES AND BISCUITS

1 When cooking cakes and biscuits the following points are important:
a. Preparation and cooking areas and equipment are ready for use and satisfy health, safety and hygiene regulations.

b. Work is planned and time appropriately allocated to meet daily schedules.
c. Cake or biscuit mixtures are of the type, quality and quantity required.
d. Mixtures are suitably prepared for the cooking process.
e. Cakes and biscuits are cooked according to product requirements.
f. Cakes and biscuits are finished in accordance with product requirements.
g. Finished cakes and biscuits are stored in accordance with food hygiene regulations.
h. Preparation and cooking areas are correctly cleaned after use.

2   Baking (pp53–7, *Practical Cookery*).
• The following key words are frequently used during the baking of cakes, sponges and biscuits. Give an example of the use of each one.

  1 Greasing: ....

  2 Marking: (a) marking shortbread biscuits with a sharp-bladed knife prior to baking

  (b) ....

  3 Loading means the economic use of oven space to ensure the maximum amount of food is organised to be baked, thus minimising .... and loss of ....

  4 Brushing: (a) egg wash on sausage rolls to improve colour and appearance

  (b) ....

  5 Cooling is the placing of freshly baked goods on wire grids or .... so that air circulates around the goods and prevents the bases becoming ....

  6 Finishing (the final finish applied to certain baked goods):

  7 Recovery time is the time required for the oven .... to reach the .... before cooking further batches of goods.

  8 Dusting: (a) sprinkling with flour

  (b) ....

  9 Glazing usually refers to the final sprinkling of certain puff pastry goods with icing sugar and returning to a hot oven for a few seconds. This causes the surface to .... and ....

3   Cakes, sponges and biscuits (recipes 7–15, pp463–6; recipe 196, p532; recipes 16–22, pp466–9; recipes 201–5, pp534–6; *Practical Cookery*).
• What is the oven temperatures for baking scones: 100°C, 150°C, 200°C, 250°C or 300°C? ....

- When testing a large fruit cake to see if it is cooked, where should the thin needle be placed and what should be the appearance of the needle when withdrawn?

....

....

....

- When baking cakes and sponges, why is it important to open and close the door gently?

....

- If cakes or sponges are moved or shaken before they are set, e.g. when half cooked, what will be the likely effect?

....

- What is the required oven temperature for baking cats tongues biscuits: 180–200°C, 230–250°C or 260–280°C? ....
- What is another name for cats tongues biscuits?

....

- When cooked, the outside edges of cats tongues biscuits should be .... and the centres ....
- When cats tongue biscuits are cooked, should they be: left to cool on the baking sheet; tipped out carefully on to a marble slab; or removed with a palette knife on to a cooling rack?

....

- What extra flavourings can be added to piped biscuits? ....
- What type of tube is used for piping out piped biscuits? ....
- After almond biscuits are baked they are trimmed with a .... and placed on to a .... using a .... knife.

4 Hygiene (see pp447–68 *Theory of Catering*).
5 Time and temperature are important when cooking cakes and biscuits otherwise finished goods will be either: undercooked, overcooked, too pale, overcoloured or unattractive in appearance; and therefore a waste of: ingredients (money), time (money), and oven heat (money).

2D9.3 **DECORATE CAKES AND BISCUITS**

1 Before decorating cakes and biscuits for service, it is important that:

a. Preparation areas and equipment are ready for use and satisfy health, safety and hygiene regulations.
b. Work is planned and time appropriately allocated to meet daily schedules.
c. Ingredients for fillings and decorations are of the type, quality and quantity required.
d. Fillings and decorations are suitably prepared for cake and biscuit decoration.
e. Cakes and biscuits are finished in accordance with product and customer requirements.
f. Cakes and biscuits are stored in accordance with food hygiene regulations.
g. Preparation areas and equipment are correctly cleaned after use.

2   Water icing (recipes 34–5, p474, recipe 67, p485, *Practical Cookery*).
3   Butter creams (recipes 191–2, pp530–1, *Practical Cookery*).
•   When making uncooked butter cream, why is it important to sieve the icing sugar?

....

•   The icing sugar and butter must be creamed until light and fluffy or creamy. Can you overbeat this mixture? Yes or no? ....
    When flavouring and colouring butter cream, the golden rule should be to flavour gently, in other words, to flavour lightly and to use colouring carefully to produce light, gentle colours. When using essences and colourings, they should never be poured directly from the bottle but poured into the bottle lid and then carefully added one or two drops at a time, mixing well in between and tasting and assessing the colour each time a few drops are added. Flavourings and colourings may also be added to mixtures with the aid of a pipette. (Examples of uses of butter cream, recipes 19–20, p468, *Practical Cookery*.)
•   How is chocolate flavour and colour added for chocolate butter cream?

....

4   Royal icing (recipe 198, p533, *Practical Cookery*). Royal icing is used in a variety of cakes, small and large. The most popular use is for celebration cakes, such as Christmas, Christening and birthday cakes.
5   Whipped cream (pp130–1, *The Theory of Catering*).

- For cream to be able to be whipped, how much butterfat must it contain?

    When whipping cream, air is beaten in and the volume increases. When using a cream with the minimum of butterfat, maximum beating is possible and therefore the maximum volume can be obtained.

    Caution: if cream is over-whipped it will separate, turn to butter and be unusable for decorating. Therefore, care must always be taken to prevent this happening.
- What would be the effect of whipping a thick double cream with 48 per cent fat content?

....

- The ideal whipping cream contains: 25 per cent, 30 per cent, 35 per cent, 40 per cent, 45 per cent butterfat? ....
- There are four rules to be observed when whipping cream:
1 It must be at room temperature or cold. Which is true? ....
2 What is the best type of bowl to use: copper, china, plastic, metal or stainless steel? ....
3 How can you prevent fresh cold cream from turning to butter when being whipped in hot conditions?

....

4 What is the safest procedure for adding cream to hot liquids?

....

- Name six uses for whipped cream.

....

....

....

6 Terms used in the various method of decorating:
a. Trimming refers to cutting the sponge or cake (if necessary) to make it even and symmetrical.
b. Filling applies to the filling of certain cakes, e.g. éclairs, profiteroles with a cream, or doughnuts with jam.
c. Spreading and smoothing are terms that are used when any icing or cream for decorating is used (recipes 19–20, p468, *Practical Cookery*).
d. Piping with icing or chocolate. Making decorative lines, spirals, leaves, rosettes, etc., to achieve an attractive finish.
e. Piping with cream. The cream must be whipped until stiff, then

placed into a piping bag, usually with a large star tube. The cream should be eased to the bottom of the bag and the top securely folded or twisted shut (if this is not done properly, the cream will ooze out of the top and on to the hands) before piping begins. To pipe, squeeze the bag gently but steadily with the right hand, and steady and guide the bag with the left hand.

Whipped cream may be left plain, or it may be lightly sweetened and lightly flavoured with 2–3 drops of vanilla essence per 250 ml ($\frac{1}{2}$ pt) of cream and called Crème Chantilly.

f.　Dusting, dredging or sprinkling. This applies to the use of icing or castor sugar in a container with a perforated lid (recipe 16, p466; recipe 44, p477; recipe 57, p482; *Practical Cookery*). It is also possible to form quick and artistic designs on certain cakes, e.g. chocolate cake, by cutting a simply patterned template the size of the cake out of white card, laying it on the cake, sprinkling generously with icing sugar and then carefully removing the template.

● Name three other cakes finished by sprinkling with castor sugar.

....

g.　Coating is completely covering the top of a large or small cake with an icing, butter cream or whipped cream. When applied, the coating should be carefully smoothed using a palette knife and, in some cases, with the cake on a turntable. For certain cakes, the sides are also coated.

h.　Topping is the final decoration, e.g. a glacé cherry or a strawberry or raspberry, on top of a rosette of whipped cream on a tartlet or a cream sponge.

● Name three other toppings. ....

7　State the differences in the following:

Royal icing　　　　　　　　　　　　Water icing

....　　...

Butter cream　　　　　　　　　　　Fondant

....　　...

Commercial fondant

....　　...

8　Design a finish to a plain Genoese gâteau, suggest a suitable filling. Use chocolate piping (fondant or butter cream). Ask your tutor or trainer for help.

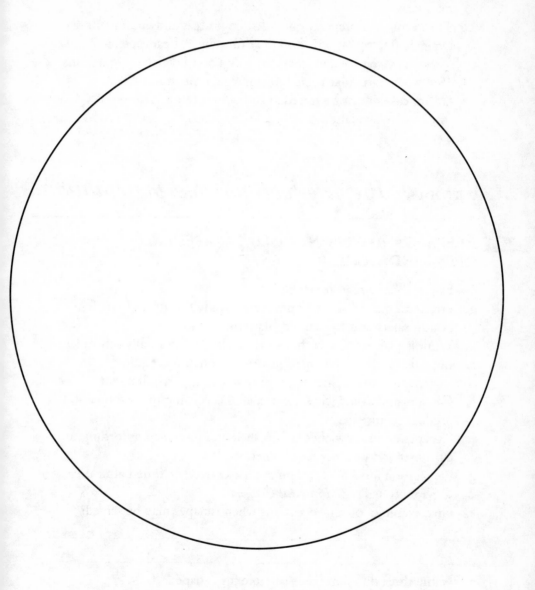

9   The contamination threats outlined in points 4 and 5 on pages 127
    and 128 are equally as relevant to the decoration of cakes and
    biscuits.

10 The keeping of preparation and storage areas and equipment
    hygienic (see pp447–52 *Theory of Catering*). (Read pp453–77, *The
    Theory of Catering*, and note carefully Food Hygiene Regulations
    1990 with particular regard to storage temperatures.)

•   Cream cakes must be stored at or below a temperature of 8°C
    (46°F). True or false. ....

UNIT 2D13   *Prepare food for cold presentation*

2D13.1 PREPARE AND PRESENT COLD CANAPÉS AND OPEN SANDWICHES

1   Essential basic requirements:

a. Preparation areas and equipment are ready for use and satisfy
    health, safety and hygiene regulations.

b. Work is planned and sufficient time allocated for daily schedules.

c. Ingredients are of the type, quality and quantity required.

d. Ingredients are prepared according to product requirements.

e. Canapés and sandwiches are prepared according to customer and
    product requirements.

f. Canapés and sandwiches are finished and presented according to
    customer and product requirements.

g. Preparation areas and equipment are correctly cleaned after use.

2   Canapés (pp142–3, *Practical Cookery*).

•   Give examples of four occasions when canapés may be served?

....

....

•   Name three different bases suitable for canapés.

....

....

•   What should be the size of canapés and why is this important?

....

•   Suggest six different foods suitable for placing on bases to make
    canapés?

....

....

- After preparing canapés what are three ways in which they may be finished?

....

....

- Suggest four fish suitable for canapés on bases.

....

- Make a list of six types of canapés which may be served hot and six that may be served cold.

Hot	Cold
....	....
....	....
....	....
....	....
....	....
....	....

- Draw six different types of canapés and describe how each should be finished.

- Name and draw eight different varieties of hot hors-d'oeuvre, labelling each.

- Name four varieties of hot hors-d'oeuvre you have recently prepared.

....

....

- Why is it important that hot canapés are bite-sized?

....

3 Vol-au-vents are large puff pastry cases usually made to a size suitable either for a first course, e.g. chicken and mushroom, or a fish course, e.g. sea-food in white wine sauce, or as a main course (recipe 78, p490, *Practical Cookery*). The small bite-sized puff pastry cases served as canapés are known as bouchées, which is a French word meaning mouthful.

4 Bouchées (recipe 82, p143, *Practical Cookery*). These may be served hot or cold and are usually referred to as cocktail savouries along with many other items, such as baby pizzas and fried fish goujons.

- Name six other cocktail savouries suitable for serving hot.

....

....

....

....

- Name six fillings suitable for cocktail bouchées.

....

....

....

....

- Fillings for bouchées should always be bound with a sauce, e.g. chicken velouté or béchamel with mushroom. Suggest a suitable sauce for the six fillings you named above?

....

....

5   Open sandwiches (recipe 84, p146, *Practical Cookery*) are popular in Scandinavian countries and an appetising variety is usually available at almost any time of day when they are eaten as a snack, as part of a meal or as a main meal according to the customer's taste and requirements.

   Open sandwiches are traditionally made with buttered thin slices of wholemeal bread on which are generously piled good helpings of freshly prepared raw and cooked foods. It is important that they always appear fresh and appetising and should therefore be prepared as close to service time as possible.
- Sketch and label six suitable toppings for open sandwiches.

• Once open sandwiches are prepared, where should they be kept prior to and during service?

....

6   The main contamination threats when preparing and storing canapés and open sandwiches are:

a. The transfer of food poisoning bacteria by using the same preparation areas, equipment and utensils for preparing cooked and uncooked products.

•   Give an example.

....

b. The transfer of food poisoning bacteria from unhygienic utensils, equipment and preparation areas.

•   Give an example.

....

c. The transfer of food poisoning bacteria from the mouth, nose, open cuts and sores and unclean hands to food.

•   Give an example.

....

d. Uncovered food contaminated by pests carrying bacteria.

•   Give an example.

....

e. Not disposing of waste or storing unused items in the correct manner.

•   Give an example.

....

7   It is important to keep preparation and storage areas and equipment hygienic to:

a. Prevent contamination of food by food poisoning bacteria.

•   Give an example.

....

b. Prevent pest infestation and unpleasant odours arising.

•   Given an example.

....

c. Ensure that standards of cleanliness are maintained.

•   Give an example.

....

d. Comply with the law.

2D13.2 PRESENT COOKED, CURED AND PREPARED FOODS

1 It is essential that:

a. Preparation areas and equipment are ready for use and satisfy health, safety and hygiene regulations.

b. Work is planned and time approximately allocated to meet daily schedules.

c. Food products and garnishes are of the type, quality and quantity required.

d. Garnishes are prepared according to dish and customer requirements.

e. Food products are prepared and presented according to customer and dish requirements.

f. Prepared dishes are stored in accordance with food hygiene regulations.

g. Preparation areas and equipment are correctly cleaned after use.

2 The typical cold meats or poultry for presentation are: roast beef, boiled or honey roast ham or gammon, roast chicken or turkey, and boiled ox tongue. These are available as left-over joints from previous hot meals; cooked specially for cold service; or bought in ready cooked from suppliers. The various ways of presentation and service are:

a. Sliced from whole joints on the bone in front of the customer (in which case all bones that may hinder carving must be removed first).

b. Sliced from boned joints, which in some cases may be rolled and stuffed (also in front of the customer).

c. Pre-sliced in the kitchen, in which case the meat or poultry should be cut as close to service time as possible, otherwise it will start to dry and curl up. Pre-sliced meats or poultry can be neatly cut, dressed with the slices overlapping each other, placed on to large dishes or individual plates, covered with cling film and kept under refrigeration. When large numbers of plated meals have to be prepared, plate rings can be used and the plates stacked in sensible sized numbers.

When joints of meat, hams, tongue or turkeys are cooked fresh for serving cold, this is usually done the day before. After cooking they are allowed to cool (the hams are left in the cooking liquor), and then kept under refrigeration overnight.

When roast chickens are required for serving cold, ideally they should be cooked 1–2 hours before service, left to cool (not in the refrigerator) and then carved as required. In this way, the meat remains moist and succulent. Chickens can then be cut into eight pieces (four leg and four breast) and the excess bones removed before serving (p87, *Practical Cookery*).

When any meats or poultry are required for a cold buffet, the joint can be presented whole with 2–3 slices cut, laid overlapping from the base of the joint, on a suitably sized dish. The two rear sides of the joint can then be garnished (if required) with two small, neatly placed bunches of watercress dressed so that only leaves show. If a little more colour is required, then a tulip-cut tomato or two may be added. It is a mistake to over garnish any cold dishes.

If the cut surface of any joint begins to look dry, a thin slice should be removed and discarded before cutting any slices for service or presenting the joint on a cold buffet.

For cold roast turkey, see recipes 14–15, pp349–50, *Practical Cookery*.

- Name four cold meats suitable for presenting and serving cold.

....

....

- If you were slicing cold meat from the remaining half of a $3\frac{1}{2}$ kilo (7 lb) joint of beef which had previously been served hot, what would you do with the first slice and why?

....

....

- When preparing joints to be carved in front of the customer, why is it important to remove certain bones first?

....

- Why when preparing a joint to be stuffed, e.g. loin of lamb, is it important to bone out the joint, add the stuffing and then roll and tie the joint?

....

- Why is it desirable to cut meat for serving cold as near to service time as possible?

....

....

- If cold meat is to be cut and presented for 500 people, what procedures would be adopted to prevent the meat from drying up and looking unappetising?

....

- Describe how a joint of roast beef can be presented.

....

- Before a turkey is roasted for service cold, what bone should be removed and why?

....

- When preparing a turkey for roasting and serving cold, is it a good idea to remove the legs, bone and stuff them and roast them separately? Give reasons for your answer?

....

....

....

....

....

- When whole hams or joints of gammon are boiled for cold service, when should they be cooked, how should they be allowed to cool and where should they be stored?

....

....

....

- If cold roast chicken is to be served moist and succulent, for lunch at one o'clock, when should they be cooked?

....

- In to how many pieces is a $1\frac{1}{4}$–$1\frac{1}{2}$ kg ($2\frac{1}{2}$–3 lb) chicken usually carved and what constitutes a portion?

....

3 Popular fish or shellfish on cold buffets include:
Salmon either whole or cut in portions (recipes 71–3, pp233–4; recipe 47, pp224–5, *Practical Cookery*).
Crab (recipe 27, p127, *Practical Cookery*).
Lobster (recipes 74–8, pp234–5, *Practical Cookery*).
Oysters (p120, *Practical Cookery*).
Smoked fish (pp96–7, *The Theory of Catering*).
Shellfish cocktails (recipe 26, p126, *Practical Cookery*).
   If a salmon is to be presented and served cold from the whole fish, the procedure is as follows:
a. Carefully remove the skin and the dark layer under the skin (which

is cooked blood). The now bared salmon flesh should be perfectly smooth.

b. Make sure the salmon is well drained and place it on to the serving dish or board.

c. The salmon is now ready for decorating and garnishing. Keep this to the minimum and avoid over-covering the fish and the dish. Neatly overlapping thin slices of cucumber (the skin may be left on or removed), quartered tomatoes (which can be peeled and neatly cut) small pieces of hearts of lettuce can, if artistically set out, give a quick, neat-looking appetising appearance. Remember time is money and there is no justification for spending a lot of time cutting fiddly little pieces of many different items to form patterns which often look untidy.

- What sauce is generally offered with cold salmon? ....
- Name four ways in which salmon may be served cold.

....

....

- What is the name given to a slice of salmon cut on the bone?
- After cooking slices of salmon on the bone for serving cold, remove the centre ...., all .... and ....
- When removing all the brown meat from the shell of a crab, what two parts should be discarded?

....

- How is the brown meat prepared?

....

- How is the shape of the crab shell neatened?

....

- Once neatened, what should be done to the crab shell before dressing the meat back in?

....

- After cutting a cooked lobster in half, what two parts should be removed before serving?

....

....

- What is the difference between cold lobster, mayonnaise sauce, and lobster mayonnaise?

....

4   Pre-prepared pâtés or terrines can be made and are available in a wide variety of types and flavourings which include liver (chicken, duck, etc.) poultry and game.

Pâtés are usually cooked enclosed in a thin layer of bacon fat (recipe 7, p121, *Practical Cookery*) or they may be enclosed in hot water pastry within a special mould.

Pâtés and terrines must be kept under refrigeration at all times and should never be allowed to stand in a warm kitchen or dining room because they are easily contaminated by food poisoning bacteria. For service, the pâté or terrine can be displayed whole with one or two slices cut, or cut in slices and dressed on plates. If in either case these are to be on display to the customer, then the display counter or cabinet must be refrigerated.

Fish and vegetable pâtés and terrines are also available. When serving meat, poultry or game pâtés, a simple garnish of a fan of gherkin and a little salad is sufficient.

5   The main contamination threats which are outlined for shellfish in points 4 and 5 on pages 127 and 128 are equally as relevant to the preparation of meat.

6   Keeping preparation and storage areas and equipment hygienic (see pp447–52 *Theory of Catering*).

•   List all the potential hygiene hazards which may occur when preparing a cold buffet starting with the raw product.

....

....

....

....

....

•   Name the control procedures you would introduce to the preparation, cooking and serving of the buffet in order to eliminate risk from food poisoning.

....

....

....

....

....

UNIT 2D14 *Prepare and cook shellfish dishes*

2D14.1 PREPARE AND COOK SHELLFISH DISHES

1   When preparing and cooking shellfish it is important to see that:

a. Preparation and cooking areas and equipment are ready for use and satisfy health, safety and hygiene regulations.

b. Work is planned and time appropriately allocated to meet daily schedules.

c. Shellfish are of the type, quality and quantity required.

d. Shellfish are suitably prepared for the cooking process.

e. Shellfish are cooked according to customer and dish requirements.

f. Shellfish are finished according to customer and dish requirements.

g. Prepared shellfish not for immediate consumption is stored in accordance with food hygiene regulations.

h. Preparation and cooking areas and equipment are correctly cleaned after use.

2   Shellfish (pp105–9, *The Theory of Catering*).

•   With the exception of shrimps and prawns, why is it best to purchase shellfish alive?

....

•   Why must cockles be soaked in salt water before cooking?

....

•   How are cockles cooked?

....

•   Suggest six uses for shrimps.

....

....

....

•   How can you distinguish prawns from shrimps?

....

•   Suggest three uses for prawns?

....

Prawns may be purchased uncooked and cooked by grilling, barbecuing, steaming, boiling or stir-frying.

- What is the difference between crawfish and crayfish?

....

- What is the difference between crawfish and langoustine?

....

- What two other names are langoustine sometimes called?

....

- What is a popular use for crawfish and why?

....

- The tail meat of crawfish can be used in the same way as the tail meat from lobsters. True or false? ....

- Lobsters and crabs have two claws. How many claws are on a crawfish? ....

- What is the general term given to shellfish soups? ....

- Crab meat is popular in many cold dishes, suggest six ways in which it may be used.

....

....

- When buying mussels, what four quality points should be looked for?

....

3 Cooking shellfish (recipe 27, p126; recipes 74–80, pp234–6; recipes 82–4, pp237–8; recipe 40, p223; receipe 13, p214, *Practical Cookery*).

- When cooking shellfish should they be plunged into cold or boiling salted water?

....

- After the white meat has been removed from a crab, it is shreded. What is the best way to do this to avoid leaving small pieces of shell?

....

- If you were required to prepare and serve six portions of dressed crab, would you dress six small crabs or one large one? Give reasons for your choice.

....

- If lobsters are allowed to overcook in boiling water, the tail flesh

can become .... and the claw meat hard and ....
....

- Name and briefly describe three cold lobster dishes.

....

....

....

....

....

....

....

....

....

....

....

There are numerous ways of serving lobster hot, e.g. soup (recipe 66, p173, *Practical Cookery*), bouchées, vol-au-vent and pasties (in which the lobster may be diced or cut into escalopes – mixed with mushrooms, optional – and bound with lobster sauce (recipe 14, p214, *Practical Cookery*). Recipes 79–80, pp235–6, *Practical Cookery*, give examples of popular hot lobster dishes served in the half shell.

- Before using, what two parts of meat must be discarded after the lobster has been cut in half?

....

- When dressing a hot lobster dish in the half shell, why is it important to place a little sauce in the bottom of the shell before the meat is added?

....

Lobsters can be grilled or barbecued, in which case they may be three-quarter boiled, removed from the cooking liquor, split in half, sprinkled with melted butter and cooked for a short period of time on or under a hot grill. If the lobsters are not pre-boiled but grilled entirely from the raw state, they will tend to become tough.

- What are the two danger signs to look for before preparing and cooking lobsters?

....

- When preparing mussels for cooking, ... the shells, ... and drain.
- If mussels are to be cooked in a thick-bottomed pan with a tight-fitting lid as soon as they have been washed, it is not necessary to add any liquid. True or false? ....
- How long will mussels take to cook over a fierce heat: 1–2 min., 2–3 min., 4–5 min. or 6–7 min?
- After mussels are cooked, what further inspection is required before they can be served and why?

....

- After mussels are cooked and drained, the cooking liquor should be retained as the basis for any sauce. True or false? ....
- To prepare a dish of moules marinière (which is one of the most traditional ways of serving them) what four ingredients are required?

....

....

- What is used to give the above sauce a light consistency?

....

Prawns, scampi, shrimp and crawfish can be cooked by shallow frying, stir-frying or deep frying. When deep fried, scampi may be passed through a light batter or flour, egg and crumbled (recipe 31, p220; recipe 40, p223, *Practical Cookery*).
- When deep frying bread crumbed scampi, why is it important to shake off all surplus crumbs and lightly roll the surfaces in order to firm them?

....

4 The main contamination threats when preparing and cooking fresh shellfish are:
a. The transfer of food poisoning bacteria by using the same preparation areas, equipment and utensils for preparing cooked and uncooked products.
- Give an example.

....

b. The transfer of food poisoning bacteria from unhygienic equipment, utensils and preparing methods.
- Give an example.

....

c. The transfer of food poisoning bacteria from the mouth, nose, open cuts and sores and unclean hands to food.
*   Give an example.

....

d. Uncovered food contaminated by pests carrying bacteria.
*   Give an example.

....

e. Not disposing of waste or storing unused items in the correct manner.
*   Give an example.

....

f. Contamination from unclean shellfish or other matter from the sea.
*   Give an example.

....

5   It is important to keep preparation and cooking areas hygenic so as to:
a. Prevent contamination of food by food poisoning bacteria.
*   Give an example.

....

b. Prevent pest infestation and unpleasant odours from arising.
*   Give an example.

....

c. Ensure that standards of cleanliness are maintained.
*   Give an example.

....

d. Comply with the law.
*   Give an example.

....

6   Time and temperature are important when cooking fresh shellfish:
a. To ensure correctly cooked shellfish dishes, e.g. cooking at too high temperature for too long will ruin any shellfish.
*   Give an example.

....

b. To prevent food poisoning.
*   Give an example.

....

c. To prevent shrinkage.
● Give an example.

....

d. To ensure that loss of nutritional value of prepared food is minimised.
● Give an example.

....

7 Dishes.
● List three shellfish dishes from Europe.

....

● Name three shellfish dishes from non-European countries with the name of the country alongside.

....

....

....

● Name any shellfish dish you are familiar with or have prepared recently giving the recipe.

....

....

....

....

....

....

....

....

....

....

....

....

....

....

8 Show by a drawing the difference between a lobster, crawfish and crayfish.

UNIT 2D15 *Cook-chill foods*

2D15.1 PORTION PACK AND BLAST CHILL FOODS

Cook-chill is a system of preparing, cooking and rapid chilling foods within a prescribed time and storing at a temperature of 0.3°C prior to re-generation immediately before serving (pp395–400, *The Theory of Catering*).

Prolonged storage for up to five days (including the day of production and the final service) can be undertaken without adversely affecting the bacteriological and eating quality of the food. Prepared chilled products where re-heating is carried out should be considered cook-chill catering. It is essential that:

a. Preparation areas and equipment are planned with hygiene in mind. They should be inspected by the local environmental health officer.

b. Equipment is in safe working order.

c. Planning makes maximum use of labour, time and materials.

d. A daily schedule is compiled to assist the planning process. Daily schedules also provide management with the product processing information. Schedules identify: dishes to be produced; production times; chilling times; and staffing. They will also identify any delays in preparation or production.

Date	**Establishment**
Dishes to be produced	*No. of portions*
1. Chicken chasseur	300
2. Navarin of lamb	250
3. Fillet of cod Duglére	300
4. Ratatouille pancakes	50

Blast chilling times
1. 1 hour
2. 50 minutes
3. $1\frac{1}{2}$ hour
4. 55 minutes

Production

Start time	*Finish time*
1. 9.15 am	2.30 pm
2. 10.00 am	1.15 pm
3. 10.30 am	12.30 pm
4. 12.00 pm	2.00 pm

Staff
James Brown
Matthew Johnson
Mary Donnely
Agnes O'Reilly

An example of a daily schedule

- Draw up your own schedule for one dish.

Date	**Establishment**
Dish to be produced	*No. of portions*
....	....
Blast chilling time	
....	....
Start time	*Finish time*
....	....
Staff	
....	....

Chilled food should be transported in refrigerated vans or insulated containers. All food must remain undamaged during storage to prevent transfer of bacteria.

- Why should chilling commence within 30 minutes of the food being cooked.

....

- Why should food be chilled down to a temperature of 3°C and the storage life not to exceed five days.

....

- If the food exceeds 5°C it must be consumed within 12 hours or discarded. Why?

....

- At a temperature of 10°C, food should be consumed
  .... or ....?

- Labelling is essential to inform the end user that the product is safe and to ensure that it is refrigerated to its prime eating quality. Complete the following label:

Name of dish	**Chicken chasseur**
No. of portions	4
Store at ....°C for max .... days	
Reheat at ....for	
in a convection oven	

Labels may also be colour coded in order to identify different dishes on certain days of the week.

- List suitable packaging containers:

....

....

....

- Dish recording is essential in order to track the process and to match the actual process to a specified process sheet. Complete the following dish recording:

Name of dish	**Chicken chasseur**
No. of portions	300
Number of chickens used	....
Storage procedures	stored at 3°C for two days
Preparation	prepared at 10°C kitchen temperature
Stored at	3°C in cold room for 24 hours
Shallow fried at	..................................°C
Simmered in sauce at	..................................°C
For	..................................min
Blast chilled at	..................................°C
For	..................................min
Portioned into	..................................containers
Stored at	..................°C for .... days

- Raw materials must be of the highest quality and freshness. Why?

....

Temperature is a crucial factor at each stage of the cook-chill process; it is important that the food is received in good condition and at the right temperature.

- How should raw items be stored?

....

- Personal hygiene and food hygiene are essential. Outline six personal hygiene procedures you would recommend when working in a cook-chill environment.

....

....

....

- Name five main course dishes suitable for cook-chill.

....

....

....

- Name five suitable desserts for cook-chill.

....

....

....

(Check the above items with your tutor.)
- In order to prevent food poisoning, which special factors have to be taken into account during the cook-chill process.

....

....

....

- Give three reasons why all food containers should be sealed and labelled correctly before storage.

....

....

....

- Portions must be controlled when filling containers because this enables the management to control costs and it avoids waste. State two other ways in which waste can be avoided:

....

- Portion control maintains a consistent standard in portion size and quality, and it maintains customer expectation and satisfaction. State two other ways you would maintain customer expectations and satisfaction.

....

....

2D15.2 STORE COOK-CHILL FOOD

1   Cooked food can be kept for five days, including the days of production and consumption provided that the temperature of the cold store is maintained at between 0°C and 3°C. Should the temperature exceed 5°C, the food should be consumed within

12 hours. Should the food exceed 10°C it must be discarded.
- For what reasons should cooked food be reheated quickly before serving?

....

....

- Food which is served cold must be consumed within ....
hours after removal from the chilled storage.
- Food once reheated must be served .... and all
unconsumed food should be ....
- What is meant by shelf life?

....

- Stock rotation procedures are essential in maintaining the delivery of a quality product. To achieve this, stock is used in order of use by date and not in excess of .... specifications.
- State why and how stock rotation will assist in reducing wastage.

....

....

....

- Stock rotation will also help to prevent food poisoning. Why?

....

....

- Storage areas must be secured from unauthorised access to prevent theft/pilferage from storage areas, and to prevent vandalism of storage areas. Name two other reasons.

....

....

2 Regenerated portioned and distributed food. If the regenerated food is consumed on site, the food in gastronorm containers can be transferred directly to a bains-marie counter from where it is served to the customer.
- Draw the module sizes for gastronorm containers (p398, *The Theory of Catering*).

Example:

← 650 mm = 2 × 325 mm →

```
┌─────────────────────────────────────┐
│                                      │   ↑
│                 2/1                  │   530 mm
│                                      │   ↓
└─────────────────────────────────────┘
```

Draw 1/1

Draw 1/6

Draw 2/3

Draw 1/3

Draw 1/2

Draw 1/4

- Give examples of cook-chill items which could be served in each module size.
  Example:
  1/1: Shepherd's pie, beef goulash
  2/1: ....
  1/6: ....
  2/3: ....

- Where satellite kitchens are involved, the distribution of chilled food requires precise organisation in order to avoid temperature fluctuation. How should temperature fluctuation be avoided in distribution?

....

- What type of equipment is required for regeneration?

....

- Chilled foods may support the growth of *Lysteria monocytogenes*. Why?

....

....

- *Lysteria* causes a food-bourne disease which can be fatal to certain groups of people. Name these groups.

....

- Why should great care be taken when reheating chilled food by microwave?

....

....

- Name any non-microbiological changes that may occur to food.

....

....

UNIT 2D16 *Cook-freeze foods*

D16.1 PORTION PACK AND BLAST-FREEZE FOODS

1 Cook-freeze production uses a system similar to cook-chill (pp400–4, *The Theory of Catering*). Recipes usually have to be modified, to enable products to be freezer stable. Modified starches

are used in sauces so that during reheating and regeneration the sauce does not separate.

- Name a suitable dish for each type of food which may be blast-frozen, giving an example of how the dish may have to be modified.

Foods	Dish	Modification
Poultry	Chicken sauté–chasseur	Sauces made with modified starch
Beef	....	....
Fish	....	....
Vegetables	....	....
Sauces	Mornay/red wine	Made with modified starch
Desserts	Chocolate mousse	....

- Why must freezing be carried out very rapidly?

....

- Food must be reduced to a temperature of at least .... °C with 90 minutes.
- Blast freezers are able to hold 20 to 400 kg per batch, what is this in imperial measurement?
  20 to 400 kg = ... to .... lb.
- Deep-freeze temperatures prevent the multiplication of micro-organism but do not .... them.
- Name two modified starches used in cook/freeze processes.

....

- The cooked food must be carefully portioned, in suitable containers. Give two examples of suitable containers.

....

- Portions must be carefully controlled when filling containers:
  To avoid ....
  To ....
  To maintain a consistent standard in the ....
  To maintain ....
- All food containers must be sealed and labelled correctly before storage to prevent contamination of food. Give four examples of

how to prevent contamination of food during the cook-freeze process.

....

....

....

....

- It is essential to ensure correct storage procedures for each type of food before processing. Why is this and give an example?

....

....

2   The cooking process is of utmost importance and will affect the overall quality of the finished product.
- In relation to the above statement, explain why time and temperature are important in the cooking process.

....

....

3   The food is divided into portions, arranged in trays and is immediately frozen.
- A blast-freezing tunnel exposes the food to a vigorous flow of .... until the items are frozen solid and the temperature is reduced to at least ....
- The reduction in temperature must take place within a period of .... hours.
- Name one other type of freezing process.

....

STORE COOK-FREEZE FOODS

Containers must protect food against oxidation during storage and allow it to be both cooked and heated quickly. They must be watertight, non-tainting and easily disposable or re-usable. Lids must be tight fitting or be machine sealable, so that no moisture is lost and the risk of microbiological contamination is virtually eliminated.
- What is the meaning of the word oxidation?

....

- Containers come in a variety of materials. List three types of materials.

....

....

....

- Containers are available as single portion packs or ....
  (name two other sizes of container).

....

- The main production unit and often the finishing kitchens in
  distribution units have deep freezers or freezer rooms where the
  food is stored once it has been frozen. These must be able to keep
  the temperature in a range from -20 to .... °C (-4 to
  .... °F).

    It is also very important that the equipment is powerful enough
  to keep the temperature at this level.

    Frozen packaged food has to be delivered to finishing kitchens at
  the same temperature that it left the deep freeze. Insulated
  containers are used for short distances, for longer distances
  refrigerated vans are used.
- Refrigerated vans maintain low temperatures by the following:
  1 By a special mechanical ....
  2 By solid blocks of ....
  3 By a system of ....
  4 By a special ....
- Name the stock rotation principles which are essential when using
  frozen products.

....

....

....

....

- The finishing kitchen is where the cook-freeze product is
  regenerated. Explain what a thawing cabinet is.

....

....

....

- Name the four types of equipment used to regenerate the food.

....

....

....

- Labels should carry the right information about the product and this information must be easily read. The information should include the production and eat-by date, storage life, instructions for use and what two other items?

....

....

- In labelling, what is meant by a disclaimer?

....

....

- Why does food separate or break up after regeneration?

....

- What would cause meat or fish to taste rancid?

....

- Why does pastry on coated food become soggy?

....

- What causes freezer burn?

....

UNIT 2D17 *Clean cutting equipment*

2D17.1 **1** Before using any type of cutting equipment it is important to understand the following:

a. Equipment *must* be turned off and dismantled before and during cleaning.

b. Work should be planned and time appropriately allocated to meet daily schedules.

c. Equipment must be cleaned in accordance with laid-down procedures.

d. Correct cleaning equipment and materials must be used.

e. Cleaned equipment must be clean, dry, ready for use and must satisfy health, safety and hygiene regulations.

f. Cleaning equipment and areas must be correctly cleaned and where appropriate stored after use.

g. Appropriate action must be taken to deal with unexpected situations within an individual's responsibility.

h. All work must be carried out in an organised and efficient manner taking account of priorities and laid-down procedures.
In addition to the equipment covered in *The Theory of Catering* (pp343–9), consideration must be given to knives and mandolines (safety rules for knives, p12, *Practical Cookery*).

Mandolines can be one of the most lethal pieces of equipment in the kitchen *if* care and common sense are not used. After use, mandolines should be carefully washed in warm or hot detergent water, rinsed in clean water and carefully dried. It is wise to think of the action of the mandoline being as drastic as that of the guillotine substituting a finger top for the head!

- Add four pieces of equipment to the list below that are classified as dangerous under the Prescribed Dangerous Machines Order 1964, and for each entry give two examples of their use:

  Worm-type mincing machine.
  Dough mixers.
  Pie and tart making machines.
  Circular knife slicing machines.

....

....

....

....

- What two documents should always be kept close to any food processing machine?

....

- Give six examples of use for the food mixer.

....

....

....

- Why should the motor of any food processing machine never be overloaded? Give one example of how this can happen?

....

- What is the tell-tale sign of a overloaded machine engine?

....

- What is the correct procedure for cleaning a machine after use?

....

- What is a vertical high-speed cuttermixer or bowl cutter? Give examples of its use.

....

....

- Food processors are versatile machines, but what is the one operation they are not suitable for? ....
- What is the function of a liquidiser or blender? Give examples of its use.

....

....

- When liquidising hot foods, e.g. soup, what precaution must be taken and why?

....

- Food slicers can be lethal if used by a careless worker. What are the five safety rules that must be followed when using a food slicer?
1 Ensure that no material likely to damage the blades, e.g. bone, is included in the food to be sliced. Otherwise the result will be to

   ....

2 ....
3 ....
4 ....
5 Extra care must be taken when the blades are exposed.
- Hand-operated and electric chipping machines are available. What is the correct way to use and maintain a chipping machine?

....

- Why should a food masher be washed, rinsed and dried immediately after use? ....
- As a general rule, all food processing machines should be dismantled after use (after switching off the electricity!) thoroughly washed, dried and re-assembled for the next use. True or false? ....
- The reasons why equipment is turned off and dismantled before cleaning are: to prevent accidents and injury, to ensure thorough cleaning, and to comply with the law. Give an example for each of these.

....

....

....

UNIT 2D18 *Prepare and cook vegetable and rice dishes*

PREPARE VEGETABLE DISHES

1   For and during the preparation of vegetables, it is important to ensure that:
a. Preparation areas and equipment are ready for use and satisfy health, safety and food hygiene requirements.
b. Vegetables are of the type, quality and quantity required.
c. Vegetables are prepared according to dish and customer requirements.
d. Prepared vegetables not for immediate use are stored in accordance with food hygiene regulations.
e. Preparation areas and equipment are correctly cleaned after use.
f. Unexpected situations are reported and dealt with in accordance with laid-down procedures.
g. Appropriate action is taken to deal with unexpected situations within an individual's responsibility.
h. All work is carried out in an organised and efficient manner taking account of priorities and laid-down procedures.

2   Vegetables (pp110–17, *The Theory of Catering*).
∘   Complete the following table by adding three examples to each vegetable type.

Classification	1	2	3	4
Roots	carrots			
Tubers	potatoes			
Bulbs	onions			
Leaves	spinach			
Brassicas	cabbage			
Pods and seeds	sweet corn			*(continued)*

Classification	1	2	3	4
Fruiting	tomatoes			
Stems and shoots	celery			
Fungi	mushrooms			
Frozen/convenience	peas			
Vegetable-protein	TVP			

3 Storage. Fresh vegetables are living organisms and will lose quality quickly if not correctly stored and handled after being harvested. It follows therefore that when fresh vegetables have been delivered to the kitchen, they should be handled and stored carefully. Roots, tubers and bulbs should be emptied from their containers and stored in bins or racks in a cool, well-ventilated store. They should be checked, and any unsound vegetables should be discarded.

Leafy vegetables, brassicas, pods and seeds (sometimes known as legumes), fruiting vegetables, stems and shoots and fungi ideally should be ordered, delivered and used daily, so that they spend the minimum time in store. If this is done and provided they are cooked correctly, then they will retain the maximum food value. In practice many of these vegetables will be stored overnight or for a few days. In all cases, they should be checked daily and any unsound vegetables discarded. Most of these vegetables are kept in a cool, well-ventilated store and, in some cases, e.g. lettuce, tomatoes and fungi, in a refrigerator.

4 Methods of preparation (pp404–50, *Practical Cookery*).
• List the five stages of making a vegetable purée.

....

....

....

• If the vegetable to be puréed has to be cut up, why is it important to cut it into roughly uniform pieces?

....

....

- Why should the vegetables only be barely covered with water?

  ....

- Name four vegetables suitable for puréeing.

  ....

  ....

- Name four vegetables suitable for stuffing.

  ....

  ....

- Without referring to *Practical Cookery*, outline the methods of preparing the four vegetables for stuffing you listed in the previous question. Check your answers with the book after you have done this.

  ....

  ....

  ....

  ....

- In order to give a neat presentation, puréed vegetables may be set into moulds.
- For a hot vegetable purée to be neatly turned out of a mould and retain its shape, the mould must be correctly prepared. It must be .... and lightly greased with .... or ....

5　The main contamination threats when preparing and storing vegetables are (see also p145):

a. products being stored at incorrect temperatures;

b. contamination from unclean vegetables.

6　Keeping preparation and storage areas hygienic (see pp447–52 *Theory of Catering*).

2D18.2　COOK AND FINISH VEGETABLE DISHES

1　Before cooking and finishing vegetable dishes the following must be observed:

a. Cooking areas and equipment are ready for use and satisfy health, safety and food hygiene regulations.

b. Vegetables are of the type, quality and quantity required.

c. Vegetables are correctly combined with other ingredients and cooked according to customer and dish requirements.

d. Prepared vegetable dishes are finished using the presentation methods appropriate to customer and dish requirements.

e. Finished vegetables not for immediate consumption are stored in accordance with laid down procedures.

f. Cooking areas and equipment are correctly cleaned after use.

g. Unexpected situations are reported and dealt with in accordance with laid-down procedures.

h. Appropriate action is taken to deal with unexpected situations within the individual's responsibility.

i. All work is carried out in an organised and efficient manner taking account of priorities and laid down procedures.

2 Cooking vegetables (pp404–50, *Practical Cookery*).

• Name two vegetables that are often roasted.

....

• What are the two ways in which parsnips can be roasted?

....

• When roasting potatoes or parsnips, heating the fat or oil before adding the potatoes lessens the chances of them sticking to the tray. True or false? ....

• Why must potatoes to be roasted be well dried on all sides before putting into the hot fat?

....

• What is the most suitable oven temperature for roasting potatoes: moderate, hot or very hot? ....

• Why is it best to turn roast potatoes and parsnips over when they are half cooked?

....

• When roast potatoes or parsnips are cooked, they must be well .... before serving.

• Describe the method of preparing, cooking and serving baked jacket potatoes.

....

....

• Baked jacked potatoes can be served as a snack meal with a variety of fillings. Name four fillings which you have seen and then suggest a filling of your choice.

....

....

- Baked jacket potatoes can also be scooped out, the cooked potato processed and cooked. Macaire and Byron are two such dishes. Briefly describe them and then suggest your own variation.

....

....

....

....

- Outline the preparation, cooking and serving of grilled tomatoes and grilled mushrooms.

....

....

Numerous vegetables can be cooked by shallow frying (Brussels sprouts, recipe 31; cauliflower, recipe 36; chicory, recipe 55; courgettes, recipe 50; onions, recipe 77; potatoes, recipes 20–22; galette, recipe 10; macaire, recipe 32; Byron, recipe 33; pp404–50, *Practical Cookery*).

- Golden rules when shallow frying vegetables:
  1 ensure the pan is ....;
  2 use a good clean fat or ....;
  3 heat the fat or .... before adding the vegetables;
  4 cook to an appetising light .... on both sides;
  5 .... lightly;
  6 finally add a light sprinkle of freshly chopped ....
- For which of the previous list of fried vegetables are the vegetables pre-cooked by boiling or steaming?

....

- For which of the above list of vegetables are the vegetables pre-cooked by baking?

....

- Which of the above list of vegetables are cooked by frying on both sides and which are cooked by sautéeing?

....

- What is meant by the term sautéeing?

....

- Those vegetables which are cooked on both sides only may

alternatively be cooked on a clean, lightly greased griddle, e.g. tomatoes and ....

Many vegetables can also be stir-fried (recipe 6, p383; recipe 23, p416, *Practical Cookery*).

- As stir-fry vegetables should only take approximately 3 minutes to cook, they must be cut into .... pieces.
- How can a good green colour be retained in green vegetables when they are to be stir-fried?

....

- As a general rule, all root vegetables are started to cook in .... salted water; those vegetables which grow above the ground are started in .... salted water.
- What is the reason for cooking green vegetables in this way?

....

- What is a quicker way of cooking vegetables than boiling?

....

- What are the advantages of cooking vegetables for as short a time as possible?

....

- What are the four factors which affect the cooking time of vegetables?

....

....

- The golden rules of boiling vegetables are:
  1 ensure they are of a .... size;
  2 use a pan of suitable size, neither too .... or ....;
  3 .... with water;
  4 lightly season with ....;
  5 cook for the .... time possible;
  6 drain off well (most vegetable cooking liquids can be used for vegetable stock if required);
  7 dry off if necessary, e.g. ....;
  8 serve as soon as possible.
- Make a list of the vegetables in recipes 21, 22, 29, 33, 46, 57, 61, 65, 66, 71, 73, 80, 91; pp404–34, *Practical Cookery*).

....

....

....

Vegetables sometimes braised include: green and red cabbage (recipes 24, 28), celery (recipe 19), chicory (recipe 56), leeks (recipe 90), onions (recipe 79) (pp404–34, *Practical Cookery*).

- List six ingredients added to green and red cabbage when braised.

  Green   Red

  ....

  ....

  ....

  ....

  ....

  ....

- Why should aluminium pans not be used for braising red cabbage (p360, *The Theory of Catering*)?

  ....

- When braising celery, what is the reason for blanching it first?

  ....

- When braising leeks, why are they tied into bunches after having been washed and before they are cooked?

  ....

- An example of cooking vegetables by stewing is ratatouille. List the ingredients and outline the method for making a dish of ratatouille.

  Ingredients   *Method*

  courgettes ....
  aubergines ....

  ....

  ....

  ....

- Give two other examples of vegetables cooked by stewing.

  ....

- All vegetables cooked by boiling may also be steamed. The vegetables are prepared exactly the same as for boiling and then placed into steamer trays, lightly seasoned with salt and steamed under pressure for the minimum period of time in order to conserve maximum food .... and retain c............................ .

Modern high-pressure steamers are ideal for this purpose (pp50–3, *Practical Cookery*) are also deep fried.

Many vegetables can be deep fried including courgettes (recipe 51), onion rings (recipe 78), salsify (recipe 85), mixed fried vegetables (recipe 96) (pp404–34, *Practical Cookery*). Then a wide range of potato dishes and shapes, e.g. crisps (recipe 23), croquettes (recipe 9), fried (chips) (recipe 28), matchsticks (recipe 25) (pp436–50, *Practical Cookery*) can also be deep fried.

- Vegetables for deep frying are passed through a light ....
- French-style fried onions are passed through .... and
  ....
- What is the difference between onions fried English and French styles?

....

- Suggest a selection of six vegetables that could be served in a mixed vegetable stir fry.

....

....

- The frying temperature for vegetables is: 160°C, 170°C, 180°C, 190°C or 200°C (pp67–71, *Practical Cookery*)? ....
- What is the term used for the partial cooking of fried potatoes?

....

- What is the purpose of partial cooking of fried potatoes?

....

- What is meant by the following terms?
  Coating: ....
  Draining: ....
  Holding for service: ....
  Spider: ....
- Why must fryers never be overfilled with fat, oil or the food to be fried?

....

- If smoke arises from a deep fat fryer, this is a danger sign of what? What should immediately be done?

....

- Why should the frying fat or oil be strained after each use?

....

- Why should fryers be covered when not in use?

....

As accidents using deep fat fryers are common in many kitchens it is important that you read and understand the rules of safety on pp70–1, *Practical Cookery.*
- Why must foods to be fried be well dried?

....

- When placing food in a fryer, e.g. pieces of fish, why must they always be placed in away and not towards you?

....

- Why is it important to have a spider and basket to hand when deep-frying food?

....

- Why should the jacket sleeves always be rolled down when frying foods?

....

3 Certain dishes of vegetables are finished by browning, e.g. cauliflower au gratin and cauliflower Mornay (recipes 40–1, p419, *Practical Cookery*). Other vegetables that can be finished in the same way include broccoli, sea-kale and marrow.
   There are various methods of finishing vegetables:
a. Glazing: when cooked vegetables such as carrots and turnips are tossed in butter over a fierce heat to give them a shine (recipe 14, p412, *Practical Cookery*).
b. Coating: this is when vegetables, e.g. cauliflower, are coated with a sauce before serving. Also braised vegetables are coated with a light sauce made from the cooking liquid (e.g. recipe 79, p427, *Practical Cookery*).
c. Colouring: this can be carried out by shallow or deep frying, placing under the salamander or in the oven.
d. Using hot sauces: in certain cases, the sauce may be poured over the vegetable; in others, it is best to serve it separately, e.g. if warm Hollandaise sauce is placed over hot broccoli in the kitchen it may curdle.
e. Using cold sauces: sauces such as mayonnaise or vinaigrette when served with cold asparagus are best served separately.
f. Garnishing: with most vegetable dishes, little or no garnishing is required as the vegetable colours are sufficient. A little chopped parsley on, e.g. sauté potatoes or savoury potatoes, may be used.

g. Piping: usually with duchesse type potatoes (recipe 8, p439; recipe 13, p440; *Practical Cookery*).

4 Main contamination threats (see p145).

5 Keeping preparation and storage areas hygienic (see pp447–52 *Theory of Catering*).

6 Time and temperature are important when cooking vegetable dishes in order to:
ensure correctly cooked vegetable dishes; prevent food poisoning; and ensure that loss of nutritional value of prepared food is minimised.

7 Draw the presentation of some vegetable dishes you have recently been involved with, e.g. purée of swede (scroll finish), braised celery (celery head, jus lié).

D18.3 **PREPARE AND COOK RICE DISHES**

1 It is important to always ensure that:

a. Preparation areas and equipment are ready for use and satisfy health, safety and food hygiene regulations.

b. Rice is of the type, quality and quantity required.

c. Ingredients are prepared and cooked according to dish requirements.

d. Prepared rice dishes are finished and presented according to customer and dish requirements.

e. Finished rice dishes not for immediate consumption are stored in accordance with laid-down procedures.

f. Preparation and cooking areas and equipment are correctly cleaned after use.

2 The versatility of rice can be illustrated by its use in the following recipes in *Practical Cookery:* 51 (p136), 37 (p164), 28 (p160), 15 (p156), 31 (p359), 32 (p360), 51 (p367), 7 (p384), 23 (p393), 132 (p513), 141 (p516), 142 (p516), 138 (p514).

Rice is the principal food crop for about half of the world's population. In order to grow, rice requires more water than any other cereal crop. There are around 250 different varieties of rice. Indian rice is long grained and tends to be dry, flaky and easily separated when cooked; Japanese is short grained, and moist, firm and sticky when cooked. Japanese rice contains more waxy starch (pp142–3, *The Theory of Catering*).

- Why is long grain rice best suited for savoury dishes and plain boiled rice?

....

- Give two examples of long grained rice.

....

Carolina type (American) rice is sometimes known as all-purpose rice as it can be used for savoury or sweet dishes.
- Why is short grain rice best suited for milk puddings and sweet dishes?

....

Arborio is one of the best-known types of short grain rice and comes from Italy.
- What is brown rice and why is it more nutritious?

....

- What is wild rice?

....

- Ground rice is used for milk puddings. Name two other products made from processed rice and give an example of the use of each.

....

....

- Why is it important to pick and wash rice, and why use plenty of boiling water for cooking (recipe 29, p257, *Practical Cookery*)?

....

- What type of dishes should always be accompanied by plain boiled or steamed rice?

....

- Why is it important to measure the amount of stock to the amount of rice when cooking a pilau (recipes 17–20, p201, *Practical Cookery*).

....

- Too much stock will make the pilau ....
- Too little stock will make the pilau ....
- In a hot oven, pilau rice should cook in approximately: 5 min., 10 min., 15 min., 20 min. and 25 min.? ....
- Why must a pilau be removed from the pan immediately it is cooked?

....

- When finally mixing in butter to a pilau, why is a two-pronged fork ideal?

....

- Why is short grain rice not suitable for pilau?

....

- Wild rice may also be braised or cooked pilau. True or false? ....
  (Recipes 18–20, p201, *Practical Cookery*, show variations on a pilau, other additions can include saffron, pre-soaked raisins or sultanas.)
- Give a suggestion of your own idea of an interesting dish of rice pilau.

....

....

The difference between a pilau and a risotto is that in a pilau the rice grains when cooked should be dryish and separate easily, in a risotto the end product is moist.
- What is the main difference in the cooking technique for a pilau and risotto?

....

- As risotto is an Italian dish, a short grain or .... rice is used. True or false? ....
- What is the finish to a risotto?

....

As with pilau, there are many variations that can be made to a basic risotto. A popular one is fish (usually shellfish) when a fish stock is used for cooking the rice.

Basmati rice is grown in the foothills of the Himalayas, this narrow long grain rice is one of the finest types of rice. Basmati should be soaked before cooking to remove the excess starch.

- List two dishes which Basmati rice could accompany.

....

....

- Steamed rice is the traditional method for preparing rice for Chinese dishes. Certain types of rice are not suitable for steaming these are:

....

- For steaming, wash the rice, and drain and dry using absorbent paper. Place the rice in a bowl and add 175 ml (.. fl oz) of water to approx. 225 g (...oz) of rice.
- Place the bowl in a rice steamer and cook over boiling water for .... minutes.
- Once cooked, the rice should be allowed to stand in the covered steamer for 10 minutes. Why is this necessary?

....

- Fried rice is cooked rice which is stir fried with other ingredients and usually finished with soy sauce. There are many different recipes and variations. List at least four different garnishes for fried rice.

....

....

3 The main contamination threats can be found under the heading Bacillus cereus on page 462 of *Theory of Catering*.
4 Keeping preparation and storage areas and equipment hygienic (see p128).
- After cooking, how should rice be stored?

....

- The spores of which micro-organism may be found in rice grains?

....

- What care should you take to prevent the growth of this bacteria?

....

....